TASTY COOKING
FOR ULCER DIETS

TASTY COOKING
FOR ULCER DIETS

by

Orlena Aagaard

GRAMERCY PUBLISHING COMPANY · NEW YORK

ACKNOWLEDGMENTS

This book is the result of ideas and contributions from many different people, along with a great deal of hard work and diligent study by the author.

The author feels especially grateful to Cameron McRae, M.D., for writing the foreword. Dr. McRae has been in the public health field for a number of years in North Carolina, Michigan, and his present location in Binghamton, New York. He has a splendid record.

Special thanks for her efficient services are due Sarah Elkin Braun, who served in an advisory capacity for this book. Mrs. Braun was formerly associated with the Michael Reese Hospital for a number of years and the Mandel Clinic in Chicago, Illinois. She is now a consulting dietitian in Evanston, Illinois.

The author also wishes to express her gratitude to the following:

Knox Gelatine, Inc., Johnstown, New York
Home Economics Services, Kellogg Company,
     Battle Creek, Michigan
Parade Publications, Inc., New York City, New York

Many of the recipes in this book were suggested by friends and relatives. A number were submitted by members of the Conrad Senior Center of Chicago, Illinois.

CONTENTS

INTRODUCTION

Peptic ulcer has aptly been called "the wound stripe of civilization," since it represents a disease rather typical of our modern, high-pressure way of life. Though the subject of much wry humor, it is no laughing matter to its victims, being one of the more difficult medical conditions to treat with success, and one which, if allowed to progress unchecked, may have serious consequences. Fortunately, medical science has learned much about the origin and treatment of peptic ulcer, so that the patient can live with a fair degree of comfort and look forward to eventual cure in most cases, if he follows his doctor's advice faithfully. But, in this even more than in most other diseases, freedom from complications and eventual recovery depend on full cooperation of the patient with his physician. And, sad to say, many ulcer patients finally "kick over the traces" because their diet seems so flat and monotonous to them that, rather than stay on it, they prefer to take their chances with the ulcer.

But "bland diets" need not be dull or monotonous. In fact, they can be made very pleasant by means of the interesting variety of dishes that can be prepared from recipes composed and selected with imagination, such as those to be found in this book.

I have known the author, Mrs. Aagaard, over a period of many years; during most of this time, we were fellow-residents of the small town of Burnsville, high in the North Carolina mountains. My family and I had the pleasure, several times, of dining with her, and always enjoyed her excellent *cuisine*. I am sure the readers of her book will find the recipes in it to be both tasty and practical; in my opinion she is rendering a real service, not only to the patient with peptic ulcer, but also to his family and his physician. As one who has specialized for a good many years in public health, I would say that this is an excellent example of health education in action.

Cameron F. McRae, M.D., M.P.H.

Mount Clemens, Michigan
March 9, 1963

FOREWORD

We hear a great deal about ulcers and bland diets. Statistics* show that every day 50,000 Americans fail to report for work because of stomach ulcers. It is estimated that this year approximately 11,000 persons will die of ulcer hemorrhages. The U.S. Public Health Service reports that there are now five times as many ulcer victims in this country as there were thirty years ago. Hence, the great need for a cook book specializing in recipes for people who have ulcers.

After a member of my own family became ill with ulcers, I began to make an extensive search for recipes using bland foods. I found some in my own files, adapted others from friends and several different sources, and created many new ones. My relative got along so well on this bland diet (combined, of course, with the medications prescribed by his doctor, and proper rest), and found the menus so palatable, that I decided to assemble the recipes into a cook book so that other ulcer sufferers might benefit from them. A book of this kind should be useful also to anyone who needs to avoid irritating foods because of other digestive disturbances. Many of the dishes, in fact, are tasty enough to appeal to the whole family, and so the housewife need not prepare two completely different menus when there is an ulcer patient in the family.

Most people have the idea that a bland diet must be dull and monotonous, but I believe that bland foods prepared according to the recipes in this book are tasty, appealing, and varied enough to result in interesting menus. The recipes range from the simple soft puddings and custards allowed on the beginning ulcer diet to the wider range of foods permitted on the advanced or permanent ulcer diet.

When an ulcer seems to be under control and no symptoms are being manifested, the patient is usually ready for the permanent ulcer diet. Recipes containing ingredients that are allowed only on this permanent diet have the words "permanent ulcer diet" enclosed in parentheses after those particular ingredients. Recipes containing such ingredients are not to be used for the beginning ulcer diet without the doctor's permission.

Ulcer patients are usually advised to eat modest portions of food at mealtime and to take light snacks between meals. In other words, the fre-

10

quency of the meals is an important factor. The ulcer patient should also exercise good judgment in his choice of foods. Though some of the dishes that are permitted are quite rich (containing whipped cream, sour cream, cream sauces, cheese, etc.), he should have the common sense not to eat two or three rich dishes at the same meal.

This book is meant to assist the person who is on a bland diet *prescribed by his doctor.* It is *not* meant to take the place of medical treatment and/or advice from a physician. Anyone who has an ulcer should first of all follow his doctor's orders carefully.

Orlena Aagaard

---

*The figures given here are from Parade Publications, Inc., New York, N.Y.

THE ULCER DIET

Always consult your physician before using any dietary list of foods. There may be foods not on this list, for instance, that your doctor will allow. Likewise, there may be foods listed here that in your particular case should be omitted.

WHAT TO EAT

Beverages

Canned fruit juices & nectars: peach, grape, apple, pear, blackberry, raspberry, apricot —usually allowed

Orange & grapefruit juice, strained and well diluted (best taken at end of meal, according to some doctors)

All forms of milk (canned, powdered, fresh whole)

Cream

Buttermilk

Weak cocoa (usually permitted)

Postum

Decaffeinated coffee (usually permitted)

Breads

Plain white bread (day-old), toasted if desired

Plain soda crackers

Rusk

Melba toast

WHAT NOT TO EAT

Beverages

Cider

Alcoholic drinks

Carbonated beverages
(none of the above without physician's permission)

Breads

Fresh, hot breads

Whole-wheat or other coarse breads

Dumplings

Griddle cakes

Waffles

Doughnuts

WHAT TO EAT	WHAT NOT TO EAT
Cakes, Icings, Cookies	**Cakes, Icings, Cookies**
Plain cakes: angel food, sponge, chiffon	Rich cakes with shortening
Whipped cream frosting, 7-minute boiled icing, fruit topping	Rich, heavy frostings
Vanilla wafer cookies	Cookies containing roughage such as nuts, raisins, coconut
Other simple cookies without too much sugar or shortening	
Cereals	**Cereals**
Cooked: strained oatmeal, strained Malt-O'-Meal, cream of wheat, rice, farina, cornmeal	Bran
	Shredded wheat
Ready-to-Serve (on permanent ulcer diet): Grape Nuts Flakes, puffed rice, cornflakes, Pablum, rice flakes, Rice Krispies	Grape Nuts
	Any cereals with roughage
Cheese, Eggs, Fats	**Cheese, Eggs, Fats**
Cottage cheese; cream cheese; mild, *soft* American cheese of cheddar or longhorn type	Hard or strong cheese
	Cheeses flavored with garlic, onion, beer, wine, caraway, etc.
Soft-cooked eggs	Hard-cooked eggs (may be permitted in later phases of the diet)
Butter or margarine	Meat fats
Vegetable shortening	
Whipping cream	
Half-and-half cream	
Desserts	**Desserts**
Cornstarch puddings	Rich desserts containing large amounts of shortening or sugar
Rice puddings	Desserts with roughage such as coconut, raisins, and fruit peel
Tapioca puddings	Spicy desserts
Junket	
Gelatin desserts	
Custards	
Ice cream, sherbet (all the above in moderate amounts)	

WHAT TO EAT	WHAT NOT TO EAT

Fruits

Strained, cooked fruits:
   peaches, plums, prunes, pears,
   blackberries, apples, apricots,
   cherries, strawberries, raspberries
Raw banana or baked banana
Dried fruits, cooked and strained
Orange & grapefruit juice, strained
   and then diluted with water

Fruits

No raw fruits (except banana)

Fish, Meat, Poultry

Beef
Liver
Lamb
Chicken
Squab
Turkey
Chicken livers
Sweetbreads
Fish
   (All the above cooked according
   to the special directions given
   later, and strained.)

Fish, Meat, Poultry

Pork
Fried meats of any kind
Canned seafood (tuna, sardines,
   salmon, mackerel, shrimp)—
   except with the physician's
   permission
Meat fats
Rich meat broths
Gravies
Stews

Macaroni, Potatoes, Other Starches

Rice
White and sweet potatoes
Macaroni
Spaghetti
Noodles

Macaroni, Potatoes, Other Starches

Fried potatoes

Pastry and Pies

Plain pie fillings: peach custard,
   butterscotch, lemon cream,
   Florida orange, cream, apple,
   tapioca, orange and lime gelatin
Piecrust made of cornflake crumbs,
   vanilla wafer crumbs, or Rice
   Krispies

Pastry and Pies

Nuts
Coconut
Raisins
Fruit peel
Heavy spices
Regular piecrust

WHAT TO EAT	WHAT NOT TO EAT

Salads and Salad Dressings
Bananas (raw)
Other fruits and vegetables,
  cooked and strained
Head lettuce, chopped fine
  (permanent ulcer diet)

Salads and Salad Dressings
Highly seasoned salad dressings
Strong condiments
Commercial mayonnaise and
  salad dressings

Soups
Fruit soups: cooked, strained
  fruits combined with a
  thickening agent
Vegetable soups: tomato puree;
  strained, cooked vegetables
  (carrots, asparagus, spinach, peas,
  cream-style corn, potatoes, wax
  beans, string beans) combined
  with a thin white sauce

Soups
Rich meat soups
Highly seasoned soups
Soups served at extreme tempera-
  tures (either *steaming* hot or *icy*
  cold)

Vegetables
Strained and cooked:
  Asparagus
  Spinach
  Young beets
  Carrots
  Lima beans
  Yellow or green beans
  Peas
  Canned cream-style corn
Mashed potatoes
Sweet potatoes
Frozen winter squash
Acorn squash
Hubbard squash
Cauliflower (permanent ulcer diet,
  if thoroughly cooked)
Cooked but *not* strained (permanent
  ulcer diet):
  Peas   Carrots
  Young beets   Spinach
        Asparagus

Vegetables
Brussels sprouts
Cabbage
Celery
Corn on the cob (unless kernels are
  split, scraped, put through blender,
  and cooked)
Onions
Old beets
Parsnips
Peppers
Sauerkraut
Turnips
In general: all raw, rough, or
  strong, gassy vegetables, except
  with the physician's permission

WHAT TO EAT	WHAT NOT TO EAT
Miscellaneous	**Miscellaneous**
Sugar, in moderation	Potato chips
Jelly	Pickles
Honey	Catsup
Strained cranberry jelly	Garlic
Salt to taste (in moderation)	Meat sauce
Milk flavored with coffee or tea	Vinegar
(sometimes allowed)	Popcorn
Flavorings (used sparingly)	Nuts or seeds
Few drops onion juice ⎱ (permanent	Coconut
Small amount of spice ⎰ ulcer diet)	Raisins
	Fruit peel

GENERAL INSTRUCTIONS
FOR PREPARING THE ULCER DIET RECIPES

All measurements for the recipes in this book should be level, unless otherwise specified. Use all-purpose flour for the cookie recipes unless cake flour is actually mentioned; a good grade of margarine or other vegetable shortening may be used in place of butter.

Cake flour should be used in all the cake recipes, and should be sifted once before measuring and three times after measuring. A triple-screen sifter that sifts the flour three times in one operation is a welcome work-saver.

When toasted bread crumbs are called for in a recipe, either rusk crumbs, Melba toast crumbs, or crumbs from toasted day-old bread may be used. Both cornflakes and cornflake crumbs are also used in various recipes.

Light brown sugar should be used in all recipes that call for brown sugar. Cornstarch is used as the thickening agent for sauces and puddings unless flour is specifically mentioned in a recipe. If desired, however, flour may be substituted for cornstarch by doubling the amount used.

In recipes where hot mixtures are to be combined with beaten eggs (either whites, yolks, or whole eggs), it is best to stir the hot mixture gradually into the eggs, a little at a time, beating rapidly after each addition.

When a recipe calls for strained cooked fruits and vegetables, there is a choice of methods. At one time, the housewife who needed to strain fruits or vegetables could only force them through an ordinary wire strainer by endless stirring with a wooden spoon. This was tedious and time-consuming. A considerable improvement was the cone-shaped metal "colander" on a standard, which came with a wooden masher in matching shape. This was a good deal quicker and less tiring to use.

Today, however, most cooks prefer to use a food mill or a blender. The food mill, a simple, inexpensive device, is operated by turning a rotating handle attached to a flat plate, which forces the fruit or vegetable pulp through holes in the bottom.

If you use a blender, be sure to follow the manufacturer's directions as to the amount of liquid necessary. In the case of fruits with seeds (raspberries and blackberries, for instance), once the blender has reduced them to a semiliquid state, they can easily be strained in an ordinary wire strainer to remove the seeds.

Finally, baby-food fruits and vegetables may be used in many recipes, saving all the time and effort of preparing your own purees.

UTENSILS NEEDED
FOR PREPARATION OF THE ULCER DIET

In addition to the usual cooking equipment, the following utensils are useful for preparing the ulcer diet:

    Food mill, for straining vegetables and fruits
    Large wire strainer for cooked oatmeal
    Meat grinder
    Blender (recommended, but not absolutely essential)
    Electric beater
    Rotary hand beater
    Onion press (for squeezing onion or celery juice for the permanent
        ulcer diet)
    2 double boilers
    Meat rack
    Pressure cooker (recommended, but not absolutely essential)
    Triple-screen flour sifter

WEIGHTS AND MEASUREMENTS

Apples, raw .... 1 pound .... 3 cups, peeled and cut fine
Bread crumbs .... 2 ounces .... 1 cup
Butter .... 1 pound .... 2 cups
Cheese, American ..... 1 pound .... 4½ cups, grated
Cheese, cottage ...... 1 pound .... 2¼ cups
Cheese, cream .... 3 ounces .... ⅓ cup
Chicken .... 5 pounds .... 4½ cups, cooked and
                                          chopped
Cornmeal .... 1 pound .... 3 cups
Cream .... 1 cup .... 2 cups, whipped
Dried fruit .... 1 pound .... Approx. 4½ cups,
                                          (varies with the fruit)
Egg whites .... 1 cup .... 8-10 egg whites
Egg yolks .... 1 cup .... 12-14 egg yolks
Flour, all-purpose ..... 1 pound .... 4 cups, sifted
Flour, cake .... 1 pound .... 4¾ cups, sifted
Gelatin, plain .... 1 envelope .... 1 tablespoon
Lemons .... 1 average size ...... 3 tablespoons juice
Macaroni and Spaghetti 7-8 ounces .... 4 cups, cooked
Margarine .... 1 pound .... 2 cups
Marshmallows .... 1 pound .... 65 to 75
Meat, cooked .... 1 pound .... 2 cups, chopped
Oranges .... 1 orange .... ½ cup juice
Oats, quick-cooking ... 1 cup .... 1¾ cups, cooked
Rice .... 1 pound .... 4 cups, cooked
Rusk .... 9 rounds .... 1 cup crumbs
Sugar, brown .... 1 pound .... 2¼ cups
Sugar, granulated ..... 1 pound .... 2¼ cups
Sugar, confectioners' ... 1 pound .... 4½ cups, sifted
Vanilla wafers .... 30 wafers .... 1 cup fine crumbs

Dash .... Less than ⅛ teaspoon
60 drops .... 1 teaspoon
3 teaspoons .... 1 tablespoon
1 ounce .... 2 tablespoons
4 tablespoons ..... ¼ cup
5⅓ tablespoons ..... ⅓ cup
8 tablespoons ..... ½ cup
12 tablespoons .... ¾ cup
16 tablespoons .... 1 cup
2 cups .... 1 pint
2 pints .... 1 quart
4 quarts .... 1 gallon

OVEN TEMPERATURES

Extremely Slow	250° to 300°
Slow	325°
Moderate or Medium	350° to 375°
Moderately Hot	400° to 425°
Very Hot	450° to 475°
Extra Hot	475° to 525°

ROASTING CHART
FOR MEATS, FISH, POULTRY

Beef	Oven Temp.	Minutes Per Pound
Medium	300°–325°	25–30
Well done	300°–325°	30–35

(Increase cooking time on boned and rolled roasts.)

Lamb (leg)		
Medium	325°	35
Well done	325°	40–45

Fish		
Baked	375°–400°	20–30

Chicken		
Chicken	325°	25

Turkey		
(12 pounds)	325°	20–25

SIZES OF CANNED GOODS

No. 1 flat	1 cup	Buffet size	8¾ ozs.
No. 2 can	2½ cups	No. 2½ can	3½ cups
No. 303 can	2 cups	No. 3 can	4 cups

SUBSTITUTES

¾ cup white corn syrup or honey .... 1 cup sugar
    (Use smaller amount of liquid in the recipe.)
½ cup evaporated milk plus ½ cup water .... 1 cup fresh milk
1 cup brown sugar, firmly packed .... 1 cup plain sugar
1 cup all-purpose flour with 2 tablespoons of
    cornstarch substituted for flour .... 1 cup cake flour
1 cup milk plus 1 tablespoon lemon juice .... 1 cup sour milk
2 tablespoons flour .... 1 tablespoon cornstarch
3 tablespoons cocoa, plus 2 teaspoons margarine . 1 ounce chocolate

TASTY COOKING
FOR ULCER DIETS

APPETITE PROVOKERS

As the name implies, "appetite provokers" should provoke the appetite. They should be made attractive to the eye as well as appealing to the taste. Strongly seasoned mixtures have been omitted, since the ulcer diet calls for soothing and mildly flavored foods.

Jelly Roll Canapés

Butter thin slices of day-old bread and remove the crusts. Spread with commercial strained cranberry sauce that has been thinned with an equal amount of whipped cream; then spread with cream cheese that has been thinned with cream. Roll in jelly-roll fashion and chill. Slice and serve.

Roast Beef Dainties

Remove the crusts from thin-sliced day-old bread and cut the bread into fancy shapes with cookie cutters. Spread lightly with butter, then with minced roast beef that has been mixed with a little Homemade Salad Dressing (see *Index*), salt, and fine-chopped hard-cooked egg. Serve cold. (Permanent ulcer diet)

Steak Canapés

Season ground steak with salt, tomato juice, and 2 or 3 drops of onion juice (permanent ulcer diet). Cut thin slices of day-old bread into various shapes. Toast the bread on one side and spread butter on the other. Spread the buttered side with a thin layer of the ground steak mixture and broil for a short time until the meat browns. Serve hot.

Toast a la Daisy

Toast slices of day-old bread. Beat egg whites until stiff and then spread on the toast. Put an egg yolk in the center of each slice. Bake in the oven until light brown. (Use as many eggs as slices of toast.)

Oven Cheese Crackers

Spread plain crackers with butter and mild, soft American cheese, grated. Put in a shallow baking pan and bake in the oven from 2 to 4 minutes or until the cheese is melted.

23

Cream Cheese Canapés No. 1

1 pkg. cream cheese
2 tsps. lemon juice
Homemade Salad Dressing
(see *Index*)

3 or 4 drops onion juice
(permanent ulcer diet)
2 hard-cooked eggs
(permanent ulcer diet)

Salt to taste

Beat the cheese. Add lemon juice, dressing, onion juice, salt, and chopped hard-cooked eggs. Serve on toast rounds.

Cream Cheese Canapés No. 2

1 pkg. (3 ozs.) cream cheese
1 egg yolk (uncooked)

Salt to taste
½ tsp. onion juice
(permanent ulcer diet)

Mix all the ingredients together. Spread on small, round crackers, and toast under the broiler.

Cream Cheese–Pineapple Canapés

Spread small rounds of toast with cream cheese thinned with pineapple syrup.

Cheese Delights

¼ lb. mild American cheese, grated
2 tbsps. melted butter

2 egg whites, beaten stiff
⅓ cup whipped cream

Add the melted butter and grated cheese to the beaten egg whites. Fold in the whipped cream. Spread on soda crackers or small squares of day-old white bread. Brown under the broiler.

Rolled Sandwich Fingers

Remove the crusts from day-old thin-sliced white bread. Mix softened cream cheese with an equal amount of strained, cooked beef or mashed, cooked chicken livers. Add a dash of salt. Spread on the bread slices and roll each one up like a miniature jelly roll. Chill.

Meringue Crackers

Small box plain soda crackers
Raspberry jelly

2 egg whites, beaten stiff
2 tbsps. sugar

Butter the crackers. Then spread with jelly and cover with a meringue made from the egg whites and sugar. Place in a shallow pan and put in a 350° oven for 12 to 14 minutes, until the meringue is light brown.

Liver Canapés

½ lb. beef liver or chicken liver
2 hard-cooked eggs (permanent
  ulcer diet)
10 soda crackers, crushed

2 tsps. lemon juice
½ tsp. onion juice
  (permanent ulcer diet)
Homemade Salad Dressing
  (see Index)

Cook the liver until tender. Grind and mix with the remaining ingredients. Serve on toasted squares of bread or plain soda crackers.

Cheese Appetizers

1 cup grated, mild American
  cheese
¾ cup milk

1 beaten egg
¼ tsp. salt
1 tsp. butter

Put the cheese and milk in a double boiler. Cook until smooth, stirring constantly. Combine part of the hot mixture with the egg, stir well, then return to the double boiler. Add salt and butter and continue to cook and stir until the mixture is smooth and thick. Serve on toast or crackers. Makes 4 to 5 servings.

Tomato–Cheese Canapés

1 cup creamed cottage cheese   1 tbsp. tomato juice
          ½ tsp. onion juice (permanent ulcer diet)

Put the ingredients in a blender and blend at high speed. Chill. Serve on soda crackers. Serves 10 to 12.

Chicken–Pineapple Canapés

Moisten strained cooked chicken with a little pineapple juice and Homemade Salad Dressing (see Index). Chill. Spread on toast squares.

SOUPS

Soup should stimulate the appetite as well as provide nourishment. There are light soups to serve with heavy meals and heavy soups that form the main part of a meal.

Meat soups are often forbidden on the ulcer diet, but milk soups made with strained cooked vegetables or strained cooked fruits provide abundant nourishment for people on this diet. Not only do milk soups introduce more milk into the diet, but the vegetables and fruits contain valuable nutrients.

Soup may be served plain or with Melba toast or soda crackers. Avoid serving hot soups too hot or cold soups too cold on the ulcer diet.

VEGETABLE SOUPS

Cream Soups

Half a cup of any of the following vegetables, *cooked and strained*, may be used to make a cream soup:

peas	wax beans
spinach	potatoes (mashed)
corn (add 2 tsps. sugar)	tomatoes
carrots	green beans
asparagus	

First, make 1 cup White Sauce (see *Sauces*). To it, add ½ cup of a strained vegetable, and stir over low heat until smoothly blended. Makes 2 small servings.

Tomato Soup

2½ cups fresh or canned tomatoes	¼ tsp. salt
⅛ tsp. soda	1 tbsp. butter
2 cups milk, heated	5 soda crackers or 1 piece dry toast, crumbled

(Cook fresh tomatoes according to the directions in the Vegetable Chart.) Strain the tomatoes. Heat to the boiling point and then add soda, hot milk, salt, and butter. Add the cracker or toast crumbs last. Serve heated. Serves 5.

Cold Borscht (Russian Soup)

2 cups fresh or canned beets
3 tbsps. sugar
2 tbsps. lemon juice

¼ tsp. salt
3 cups water
¾ cup sour cream

Cook fresh beets according to the directions in the Vegetable Chart and reserve the cooking liquid. Strain the beets. Then mix with the beet juice, sugar, lemon juice, salt, and water, and bring to a boil. Remove from heat and chill. Add sour cream to the beet mixture and beat well. Float 1 spoonful of sour cream on top of the soup when serving. Serves 5.

Red Velvet Beet Soup

2 bunches beets (about
   8 medium-size beets)
2 cups cold water
2 tbsps. butter

2 tbsps. sugar
½ tsp. salt
2 tbsps. cornstarch
4 cups milk

Cook the beets in 2 cups of water according to the directions in the Vegetable Chart. Drain off the cooking liquid and reserve. When the beets are cool enough to handle, slip off the skins, stems, and roots and cut the beets into fairly small pieces. Put these into a blender, along with the reserved cooking liquid, and blend until smooth.

Melt the butter, add the sugar, salt, and cornstarch, and stir until smooth. Slowly stir in the milk and cook over low heat until thickened, stirring constantly. Combine with the beet mixture and reheat. Serves 8 to 10.

Corn–Tomato Chowder

2 cups cream style canned corn,
   strained
2 cups canned tomatoes,
   strained
4 medium potatoes, cubed
   and cooked

1 tsp. onion juice
   (permanent ulcer diet)
1 tbsp. sugar
2 cups White Sauce
   (see *Sauces*)
5 soda crackers, crushed

Combine all the ingredients and cook over low heat for a few minutes. Add the soda crackers last. Serve hot. Serves 6 to 8.

Creamed Tomato Soup

No. 303 can tomatoes,
  strained

2 cups White Sauce—double
  batch (see *Sauces;* use
  half milk and half cream)

Mix the hot White Sauce with the strained tomatoes. Heat and stir. Serves 5.

Green Bean—Potato Soup

No. 303 can green beans,
  strained

3 medium-size potatoes,
  cooked and mashed

2 cups White Sauce—double batch (see *Sauces;* use half milk and
  half cream)

Add the strained beans and the mashed potatoes to the hot White Sauce and mix thoroughly. Serve hot. Serves 6.

Carrot—Pea Soup

1 cup canned peas, strained

1 cup cooked carrots, strained

2 tbsps. quick-cooking rice

Dash of salt

4 cups milk

2 cups White Sauce

  (see *Sauces*)

1 beaten egg

5 soda crackers, crushed

Combine the peas, carrots, rice, salt, and milk. Cook gently over low heat for a few minutes.

Add a small amount of the hot White Sauce to the beaten egg and stir; then add to the remaining sauce. Combine with the hot vegetable mixture. Add the crushed soda crackers last. Serve hot. Serves 6.

Creamed Potato Soup

1 sliced hard-cooked egg
  (permanent ulcer diet)

½ tsp. onion juice
  (permanent ulcer diet)

½ tsp. salt

3-4 medium potatoes, diced

2 cups White Sauce
  (see *Sauces*)

Cook the potatoes according to the directions in the Vegetable Chart.

Drain. Add slices of hard-cooked egg, the onion juice, and salt to the White Sauce. Combine with the potatoes. Thin the soup with additional milk if desired. Serves 5.

Sour Cream–Potato Soup

3 potatoes, sliced
1 cup sour cream (may be
thinned with milk)

½ tsp. onion juice
(permanent ulcer diet)
1 egg, beaten

Cook the potatoes in small amount of water until tender. Drain. Mix the sour cream and onion juice with the beaten egg. Pour over the potatoes, heat, and serve. Serves 4.

FRUIT SOUPS

Raspberry Soup

2 pkgs. frozen raspberries
(10 ozs. each)
2 cups water
½ cup sugar

2½ tbsps. quick-cooking
tapioca
Dash of salt
1 tbsp. lemon juice

Bring the raspberries to a boil, simmer 10 minutes, and then strain. Discard seeds. Place the fruit pulp and juice in a saucepan. Add the water, sugar, tapioca, and salt, and bring to a boil over medium heat. Remove and add lemon juice. Chill. Serves 5.

George Washington Soup

No. 303 can pitted sour red
cherries, strained
⅔ cup sugar

Dash of salt
2 tbsps. cornstarch
1 tbsp. lemon juice

3 cups milk, heated

Mix sugar, salt, and cornstarch. Thoroughly blend in the strained cherries and lemon juice, a little at a time. Cook in a double boiler until thickened, stirring constantly. Add heated milk and stir well. Serve either hot or cold. Serves 4 to 5.

Fresh Cherry Soup

4 cups cooked fresh cherries,
  strained
¼ cup quick-cooking tapioca
1⅓ cups hot water

4 cups water
⅔ cup sugar
2 tbsps. lemon juice
1 egg yolk

Put tapioca and 1⅓ cups hot water in a saucepan and cook until transparent. Add strained cherries, along with their juice, 4 cups water, sugar, and lemon juice. Simmer for 10 to 15 minutes. Remove from fire, strain, and add beaten egg yolk. Serve warm or cold. Serves 6 to 8.

Pineapple Soup

1 cup pineapple juice
2 tbsps. quick-cooking tapioca

1 cup water
1 tbsp. sugar

1 tbsp. lemon juice

Combine tapioca and 1 cup of water in a saucepan. Cook and stir over medium heat until the mixture comes to a boil. Remove from heat. Add sugar, pineapple juice, and lemon juice. Stir to blend. Cover and chill. Serves 4.

Orange Fruit Soup

⅓ cup orange juice
3 jars baby-food peaches
1 medium banana, sliced

2 tbsps. quick-cooking tapioca
1½ cups water
1 tbsp. sugar

Mix the tapioca and water in a saucepan. Cook and stir over medium heat until the mixture comes to a boil. Remove from heat, add sugar and orange juice, and stir to blend. Cover and chill. Before serving, stir in the peaches and banana slices. Serves 4 to 5.
Variations: Substitute apricot nectar for orange juice. Serve with whipped cream on top.

Fruit Refresher Soup

No. 2½ can soft apricots, undrained
No. 2½ can purple plums, pitted but
  undrained

2 tbsps. orange juice
Juice of ½ lime
2 tbsps. white corn syrup

FRUIT SALADS

Banana Salad

2 ripe bananas
1 tbsp. lemon juice
½ cup water

Fruit Salad Dressing (see *Index*),
whipped cream, or
cottage cheese

Combine the lemon juice and water. Cut the bananas into serving portions and dip in the lemon-juice mixture to keep from turning dark. Serve with the Fruit Salad Dressing, whipped cream, or cottage cheese. Serves 3 to 4.

Apricot Salad

No. 303 can soft apricot halves
(permanent ulcer diet)

1 large carton cottage cheese

Put a mound of cottage cheese on finely shredded lettuce (permanent ulcer diet). Place apricot halves on top of the cheese. Serves 4 to 5.

Canned Peach Salad

No. 303 can soft peach halves
(permanent ulcer diet)

1 pkg. cream cheese (3 ozs.)
Cream or orange juice

Mash the cream cheese, adding a little cream or orange juice to thin. Chill. Serve poured over peach halves on finely shredded lettuce (permanent ulcer diet). Serves 4 to 5.

Cottage Cheese–Peach Salad

1 large carton creamed
cottage cheese

No. 303 can sliced Elberta
peaches

Put a large dipper of creamed cottage cheese on shredded head lettuce and arrange the peach slices around the cheese to look like flower petals. Serves 4 to 5. (Permanent ulcer diet)

Party Salad

2 beaten eggs
¼ cup sugar
1 tbsp. butter
14 diced marshmallows
¼ tsp. almond extract

½ cup cream, whipped
1 cup white cherries, pitted
   (permanent ulcer diet)
½ cup chopped canned pears
   (permanent ulcer diet)

2 tsps. maraschino cherry juice

Cook the eggs, sugar, butter, and marshmallows in a double boiler until thick, stirring constantly. Remove from heat and cool for a few minutes. Fold in the whipped cream and flavoring. Mix together the white cherries, chopped pears, and maraschino cherry juice and combine with the cooked mixture. Chill. Serves 5.

Fruit Cocktail Cups

2 sliced bananas
1 cup white cherries, drained and
   pitted (permanent ulcer diet)
½ cup chopped canned pears
   (permanent ulcer diet), drained

2 tsps. lime juice
1 recipe Vanilla Custard
   (see *Sauces*)
6 oranges (cut into halves and
   pulp removed)

Blend the drained fruits and the lime juice with the custard. Fill the orange cups and chill. Set the cups in a pan with ice for a few minutes before serving time. Serves 4 to 5.

Orange–Grape Mold

1 pkg. orange gelatin
1 cup boiling water
¾ cup grape juice

¼ cup cold water
1 pkg. cream cheese (3 ozs.)
8-10 diced marshmallows

Sweetened whipped cream

Dissolve the gelatin in boiling water. Add grape juice and cold water and stir well. Chill until the gelatin begins to congeal. Then add the cream cheese made into 1-inch balls, and the marshmallows. Pour into a mold and chill. Serve with a spoonful of whipped cream on top. Serves 5.

Lemon–Cranberry Mold

1 pkg. lemon gelatin
1 cup boiling water
¾ cup cold water

½ can strained cranberry sauce
½ cup cream, whipped and
   sweetened

Dissolve the gelatin in boiling water. Stir in cold water. Chill until the gelatin begins to congeal. Then add the cranberry sauce (cut into small pieces). Set the bowl in a larger bowl with ice water and whip until fluffy. Fold in the whipped cream, pour into a mold, and chill. Serves 5.

Strawberry–Pineapple Mold

1 pkg. strawberry gelatin
1 cup boiling water
½ cup pineapple juice

1 cup sweetened, slightly cooked
   strawberries, strained
¼ cup cream, whipped

Dissolve the gelatin in boiling water. Stir in the pineapple juice and chill until the gelatin begins to congeal. Then add the strained strawberries and their juice. Fold in the whipped cream, pour into a mold, and chill. Serves 5.

Lemon–Apple Mold

1 pkg. lemon gelatin
1 cup boiling water
½ cup apple juice

½ cup canned applesauce
   (with 2 tsps. honey)
Dash cinnamon (permanent ulcer
   diet)

¼ cup cream, whipped

Dissolve the gelatin in boiling water. Stir in the apple juice and chill until the gelatin begins to congeal. Then add the applesauce and cinnamon; fold in the whipped cream last. Pour into a mold and chill. Serves 5.

Orange–Cheese Ball Mold

1 pkg. orange gelatin
1 cup boiling water
1 cup cold water

½ can strained cranberry
   sauce, chilled
1 pkg. cream cheese (3 ozs.)

Dissolve the gelatin in hot water. Add the cold water and stir well. Chill until the gelatin begins to congeal. Then add the cranberry sauce cut into cubes. Form the cream cheese into small balls and add them to the gelatin mixture. Pour into a mold and chill. Serves 5.

Lime–Cherry Mold

1 pkg. lime gelatin
1 cup boiling water
¾ cup fruit syrup
   (add water if necessary)
1 tbsp. lemon juice

1 cup creamed cottage cheese
1 cup mixed canned fruit
   (pears, peaches, and Bing
   cherries), strained
½ cup cream, whipped and
   sweetened

Dissolve the gelatin in boiling water. Add the fruit syrup and lemon juice and chill until the gelatin starts to congeal. Then fold in the cottage cheese, fruit, and whipped cream. Serves 5.
Variations: Use lemon or orange gelatin and strained peaches or strained apricots.

Cherry Foam

1 pkg. cherry gelatin
1 cup boiling water
1 cup cold water

½ cup cream, whipped
2 sliced bananas
8-10 diced marshmallows

½ tsp. vanilla extract

Dissolve the gelatin in boiling water. Add the cold water and chill until the gelatin begins to congeal. Then fold in the whipped cream, bananas, marshmallows, and flavoring. Pour into a large mold and set in the refrigerator until serving time. Serves 5.

Orange–Peach Gelatin Salad

No. 2 can soft peach halves
   (permanent ulcer diet)
1 pkg. cream cheese (3 ozs.)

1 can strained cranberry sauce
1 pkg. orange gelatin
1 cup boiling water
1 cup cold water

Arrange the peach halves in a salad mold. Blend together the cream cheese and cranberry sauce, using a little cream to thin, if necessary. Fill the peach cavities with the mixture.

Dissolve the orange gelatin in boiling water. Then stir in the cold water. Pour over the peaches and chill until serving time. Serves 5.

Orange–Peach Marlborough Salad

1 pkg. orange gelatin
1 cup boiling water
No. 303 can soft peaches
½ cup cream, whipped

1 pkg. whipped cream cheese
   (3 ozs.)
9 diced marshmallows
¼ tsp. vanilla extract

Dissolve the gelatin in hot water. Drain the peaches and mash well. Add peaches and ½ cup peach juice to the gelatin. Pour into a mold and chill until serving time.

When ready to serve, unmold on finely chopped head lettuce (permanent ulcer diet). Combine the whipped cream, cream cheese, marshmallows, and flavoring and use as a topping. Serves 5.

Florida Salad

1 pkg. lemon or orange gelatin
1 cup boiling water
½ cup orange juice

½ cup pineapple juice
1 cup cream, whipped
2 bananas, mashed
6 marshmallows, diced

Dissolve the gelatin in the boiling water. Let cool, then add the orange and pineapple juice and chill until the gelatin starts to congeal. Add the whipped cream, bananas, and marshmallows last. Chill until serving time. Serves 5.

Raspberry—Banana Mold

1 pkg. raspberry gelatin
2 ripe bananas, sliced

1 cup boiling water
1 cup cold water or fruit juice

Dissolve the gelatin in boiling water. Add the cold water or fruit juice and chill until the mixture starts to congeal. Then add the sliced bananas. Chill until serving time. Serves 5.

Pineapple Mystique Salad

8½-oz. can crushed pineapple, undrained
1 pkg. orange gelatin

1 cup boiling water
Juice of ½ lemon
½ cup cold water

1 cup dairy sour cream

Dissolve the gelatin in boiling water. Then stir in the lemon juice and chill. Put the cold water and canned pineapple in a blender and blend for a minute or two. When the chilled gelatin begins to congeal, add the pineapple and the sour cream and stir until well mixed. Pour into a mold. Serves 5.

Bing Cherry Salad

1 can black Bing cherries
1 pkg. cherry gelatin

½ cup sugar
1 cup boiling water

Drain the cherries and reserve the juice. Strain the cherries. Add the sugar to the gelatin and dissolve in the boiling water. Add ½ cup of the reserved juice and stir well. Cool. When the gelatin starts to congeal, add the strained fruit and pour into a mold. Chill. Serve with the following dressing:

¼ cup sugar
2 tsps. cornstarch
2 beaten eggs

⅔ cup pineapple juice
Juice of 1 orange
⅛ cup cream, whipped

Mix the sugar and cornstarch. Stir in the beaten eggs gradually, to make a paste. Add the fruit juices and cook in a double boiler until thick, stirring constantly. When the dressing has cooled, add the whipped cream. Serves 5.

VEGETABLE SALADS

Tomato Aspic

1 envelope unflavored gelatin
¼ cup cold water
1½ cups hot tomato juice
1 tbsp. sugar
2 tsps. lemon juice

1 tsp. onion juice
   (permanent ulcer diet)
½ tsp. celery juice
   (permanent ulcer diet)
¼ tsp. salt

Mix the gelatin with the cold water to soften. Add the hot tomato juice and stir well to dissolve. Stir in the sugar, lemon juice, onion juice, celery juice, and salt. Turn into a mold and chill. Serves 4 to 5.

Spinach-Egg Mold

2 cups cooked spinach, drained
2 sliced hard-cooked eggs
   (permanent ulcer diet)
1 pkg. lemon gelatin
1 tbsp. granulated sugar

1 cup boiling water
½ cup cold water
1 tbsp. lemon juice
¼ tsp. salt
½ cup sour cream

Dissolve the gelatin and sugar in boiling water. Stir in the cold water and lemon juice and chill until the gelatin begins to thicken. Arrange hard-cooked egg slices and spinach in the bottom of a mold. Sprinkle with salt. Fold the sour cream into the gelatin mixture and pour over the spinach and eggs. Chill. Serves 5 to 6.

Beet–Egg Salad

8-oz. can small, whole beets
   (permanent ulcer diet)
2 hard-cooked eggs, sliced
   (permanent ulcer diet)

1 pkg. lemon gelatin
2 tsps. sugar
1 cup cold water
Juice of 1 lemon

Drain the juice from the beets, and to it add enough water to make 1 cup. Heat to boiling and pour over the gelatin. Add the sugar and stir until thoroughly dissolved; then add the cold water and mix well. Stir in the lemon juice last. Let the gelatin mixture cool slightly.

Arrange the egg slices and beets in a mold. Pour the cooled gelatin mixture on top and chill until set. Serves 5 to 6.

Orange–Beet Salad

1 pkg. orange gelatin	¼ tsp. salt
2 cups strained cooked beets	2 tbsps. orange juice
1 cup boiling water	½ tsp. onion juice
¾ cup sour cream	(permanent ulcer diet)

Dissolve the gelatin in boiling water. Cool for a few minutes; then add the strained beets and their juice. Fold in the sour cream, salt, orange juice, and onion juice. Pour into a mold and chill. Serve on chopped lettuce (permanent ulcer diet) with a dab of sour cream on top. Serves 5.

Hot Potato Salad

2 cups hot mashed potatoes (unseasoned)	2 tbsps. lemon juice
2-3 tbsps. Homemade Salad Dressing (see Index)	2 tsps. sugar
	1 tsp. onion juice (permanent ulcer diet)
½ tsp. salt	

Mix all the ingredients together and serve hot. Serves 4.

MISCELLANEOUS SALADS

Cottage Cheese–Egg Salad

Arrange slices of hard-cooked egg (permanent ulcer diet) on a dipper of cottage cheese set on finely shredded head lettuce (permanent ulcer diet). Spoon homemade Pineapple Salad Dressing (see Index) over the top and garnish with grated cheese. Serve half an egg and 1 scoop of cottage cheese per person.

Hot Macaroni Salad

2 cups cooked macaroni	1 tsp. onion juice (permanent ulcer diet)
1 cup Tomato Sauce (see Sauces)	1 tsp. celery juice
2 tsps. sugar	½ tsp. salt
1 tbsp. lemon juice	2 sliced hard-cooked eggs

Mix the hot macaroni with all the other ingredients, reserving one egg to garnish the top. Serves 4.

Fish Salad

1-lb. pkg. frozen halibut,
  cooked and flaked
2 hard-cooked eggs, sliced
  (permanent ulcer diet)
1 tsp. lime juice
3 tbsps. orange juice, strained

3-4 tbsps. Homemade Salad Dressing
  (see *Index*)
½ tsp. salt
½ tsp. onion juice
  (permanent ulcer diet)

Combine the fish with the other ingredients and mix well. Chill. Serve individual portions of the fish mixture on finely shredded head lettuce (permanent ulcer diet). Serves 5 to 6. (Use an ice cream dipper or scoop to dip the portions of salad.)

Variation: Use tomato juice in place of the citrus fruit juices.

SALAD DRESSINGS

UNCOOKED SALAD DRESSINGS

Cottage Cheese Dressing

1 cup creamed cottage cheese
2 tbsps. sugar

1 tsp. lemon juice
2 cups sour cream

¼ tsp. salt

Mix the ingredients together and chill. Makes about 2½ cups.

Variation: Add hard-cooked egg slices and ½ teaspoon onion juice (permanent ulcer diet).

Sour Cream Dressing

1 cup sour cream
1 tbsp. strained honey

2 tbsps. sugar
2 tbsps. lemon juice

Mix the ingredients together and chill. Makes about 1 cup.

Marshmallow–Cranberry Dressing

½ cup strained cranberry sauce
½ cup whipped cream

2 tbsps. marshmallow creme
1-2 drops orange extract

Combine the whipped cream, marshmallow creme, and flavoring with the cranberry sauce. Chill. Makes about 1 cup.

Maraschino Cherry Dressing

¼ cup maraschino cherry juice   1 cup sour cream, or ½ cup
10 diced marshmallows   sweet cream, whipped

Pour the cherry juice over the marshmallows, cover the dish, and let stand for 5 minutes. Then mix with the whipped or sour cream and chill. Makes 2½ cups.

COOKED SALAD DRESSINGS

Lemon Dressing for Fruit Salad

⅔ cup sugar   1 cup milk
1 tbsp. cornstarch   1 egg

Juice ½ lemon

Mix the sugar and cornstarch; add a little milk to make a paste. Then beat the egg into the mixture. Add the remainder of the milk and cook until thick, stirring constantly. Cool; then add lemon juice. Makes about 1¼ cups.

Homemade Salad Dressing

2 tbsps. sugar   1 tsp. onion juice
¼ tsp. salt   1 tbsp. butter
1 tbsp. flour   2 tbsps. lime juice
1 beaten egg   2 tbsps. lemon juice
1 tsp. celery juice   ¼ cup half-and-half cream

Mix the dry ingredients together and then combine with the beaten egg. Add the celery and onion juice and the butter. Gradually stir in the fruit juices. Cook in the top of a double boiler until thickened, stirring constantly. Remove from the heat and add half-and-half cream. (Thin with additional cream if desired.) Cool. Store in the refrigerator until ready to use. Makes about ¾ cup.

Boiled Lemon Dressing

⅓ cup sugar   4 beaten eggs
1 tbsp. cornstarch   ½ cup lemon juice
¼ tsp. salt   2 tbsps. melted butter

Blend the sugar, cornstarch, and salt with the beaten eggs. Slowly add the lemon juice and melted butter. Stir constantly and cook until thickened. Thin with pineapple juice or cream if too thick. Makes about 1 cup.

Pineapple Salad Dressing

½ cup sugar   1 beaten egg
Dash of salt   ½ cup pineapple juice
1 tbsp. cornstarch   3 tbsps. lemon juice
              1 cup evaporated milk, chilled and whipped

Mix sugar, salt, and cornstarch with the beaten egg. Gradually add the pineapple and lemon juice. Cook in a double boiler until thick. Remove from heat, cool, and add whipped evaporated milk. Makes about 1¼ cups.

Honey–Marsh Salad Dressing

4 beaten egg yolks   2½ tbsps. lemon juice
½ cup strained honey   10 diced marshmallows
                ½ cup cream, whipped

Stir the honey into the egg yolks. Add the lemon juice. Cook in a double boiler until the mixture thickens. Remove from heat and add the marshmallows. Cool. Fold in the whipped cream last. Makes about 1 cup.

Honey Salad Dressing

1 tbsp. cornstarch   2½ tbsps. lemon juice
1 tbsp. sugar   ½ cup strained honey
1 beaten egg   ½ cup cream, whipped

Mix the cornstarch and sugar; add the beaten egg, lemon juice, and honey. Cook in a double boiler until the mixture thickens. Cool; then add whipped cream. Makes about 1 cup.

Salad Dressing For Fruits

2 eggs, beaten very light   ¼ cup lemon juice
¼ cup orange juice   ½ cup sugar (scant)

Cook the ingredients in a double boiler until thick. Thin with cream if necessary. Makes about ¾ cup.

Fruit Salad Dressing

1 tbsp. cornstarch   Juice of 1 lemon
¼ cup sugar   2 well-beaten egg whites
                    ½ pt. cream, whipped

Mix the cornstarch, sugar, and lemon juice into a paste and slowly bring to a boil. Cool slightly. Fold into the stiffly beaten egg whites. Fold in the whipped cream last. Makes about 2½ cups.

Tropical Salad Dressing

¼ cup sugar   ¼ cup pineapple juice
1 tbsp. cornstarch   ¼ cup orange juice
2 tbsps. cold water   Juice of ½ lemon
1 beaten egg   ¼ cup cream, whipped

Mix together the sugar and cornstarch; add the cold water and stir into a paste. Add the beaten egg. Then stir in the fruit juices and cook until thick, stirring constantly. Remove from heat, allow to cool, and add whipped cream. Makes about 1 cup.

Marlborough Fruit Dressing

2 beaten eggs   16 diced marshmallows
¼ cup sugar   ¼ tsp. vanilla extract
2 tbsps. butter   ½ cup cream, whipped

Cook all the ingredients, with the exception of the whipped cream and the flavoring, in a double boiler until thick. Then remove from the heat and allow to cool. Add whipped cream and vanilla. Fold in any kind of cooked fruit allowed on this diet.

FISH AND SHELLFISH

Fish is an important source of protein for the ulcer diet. It also furnishes certain vitamins in the vitamin B family, and phosphorus, iron, and other minerals.

Many different kinds of frozen fish are now available, and these can be quickly and easily prepared by the busy housewife. For the ulcer diet, fish should be baked, boiled, or broiled. When fish is boiled, the water should be only simmering. Broiling is about the fastest and simplest method of cooking fish.

Broiled Fish

1-lb. pkg. frozen sole fillet   ½ tsp. salt
   or halibut   1 tbsp. butter

Cut the fish into serving-size portions. Sprinkle with salt and brush with butter. Place fish, skin side down, on a preheated, greased broiler pan about 3 inches from the heat. Baste with lemon juice if desired. To broil usually takes between 15 and 20 minutes. Serves 3 to 4.

Plain Boiled Fish

1-lb. pkg. frozen halibut   ½ tsp. salt
1 slice lemon   1 carrot
1 stalk celery   1 slice onion
3-4 cups water

Wrap the halibut in cheesecloth. Put in a saucepan with all the other ingredients and simmer until the fish is tender enough to fall apart. Remove from the water and unwrap. Place in a hot serving dish and serve with White Sauce (see Sauces) to which chopped hard-cooked egg slices (permanent ulcer diet) have been added. Serves 3 to 4.

Baked Fish

Unwrap a 1-lb. package of frozen sole fillets and place them in a greased baking dish. Spread with softened butter and sprinkle lightly with salt. Bake in a hot (400°) oven for 35 to 45 minutes. Serves 3 to 4.

Baked Sole Fillet au Gratin

1-lb. pkg. frozen sole fillets   1 tbsp. butter
½ tsp. salt   1 cup grated, mild American cheese
                   Toast crumbs

Put the frozen fish in a baking pan. Salt, and dot with butter. Bake in a 400° oven for 20 minutes. Cover with toast crumbs and grated cheese. Lower heat to 350° and continue baking for 15 to 20 minutes or until fish is done. Serves 3 to 4.

Corn-Crisped Fish

1-lb. pkg. frozen sole fillets   1 cup cornflake crumbs
½ cup milk   4 tsps. corn oil or melted
1 tsp. salt   butter

Cut the fish into serving-size pieces. Combine the milk and salt. Dip the pieces of fish in the milk, then in cornflake crumbs. Arrange on a well-oiled baking sheet or in a shallow pan and sprinkle with corn oil.

Bake in a moderate oven (375° to 400°) about 20 minutes or until tender. Serve immediately. Serves 3 to 4.

Orange Baked Fish

1-lb. pkg. frozen halibut   1 tbsp. butter
½ tsp. salt   ⅓ cup strained fresh orange juice

Put the frozen halibut in a greased casserole. Sprinkle with salt and brush with butter. Pour the orange juice over the fish. Baste once or twice during baking process. Bake in a 400° oven for 25 to 30 minutes. Serves 3 to 4.

Baked Orange–Sole Fillets

1-lb. pkg. frozen sole fillets   2 tsps. melted butter
½ tsp. salt   1 recipe Orange Sauce
                                          (see *Sauces*)

Put the fillets in a greased casserole. Sprinkle with salt and spread with butter. Bake in a 400° oven for 25 to 30 minutes. Serve with Orange Sauce that has been heated. Serves 3 to 4.

Baked Cod Loaf

1-lb. pkg. frozen codfish,
   cooked

1 cup White Sauce
   (see *Sauces*)

2 cups canned tomatoes,
   strained

1 tsp. onion juice
   (permanent ulcer diet)

½ cup toast crumbs

1 tbsp. melted butter

⅔ cup grated, mild American
   cheese

½ tsp. salt

Add the tomatoes and onion juice to White Sauce and cook until smooth. Place the fish in a greased casserole; cover with the sauce. Add salt. Spread toast crumbs, butter, and cheese on top. Bake in moderate (350°) oven for 25 to 30 minutes. Serves 4 to 5.

Fish Casserole

1-lb. pkg. frozen fillet of sole
   or halibut

½ tsp. salt

1 cup White Sauce (see *Sauces*)

2 cups seasoned mashed potatoes

½ cup grated, mild American
   cheese

½ cup cornflakes

2 tsps. butter

Put fish in 4 cups of salted cold water and cook until tender enough to fall apart. Add the fish to the White Sauce and mix well. Make alternate layers of fish and mashed potatoes in a greased casserole. Cover the top with grated cheese, cornflakes, and melted butter. Bake in a 350° oven for 25 to 30 minutes. Serves 4 to 5.

Halibut—Rice Pudding

1 cup flaked cooked halibut

1 cup cooked rice

1 cup canned tomatoes, strained

⅔ cup grated, mild American
   cheese

½ tsp. salt

1 cup half-and-half cream

½ cup toast crumbs

1 tbsp. butter

Place halibut, rice, tomatoes, and cheese in alternate layers in a greased casserole. Add salt. Pour half-and-half cream over the top. Cover with buttered crumbs. Bake in a 350° oven for 30 minutes. Serves 4 to 5.

Codfish Balls

1-lb. pkg. frozen cod fillets,
  cooked and flaked
1 recipe Mashed Potatoes
  (see *Vegetables*)

1 cup White Sauce
  (see *Sauces*)
½ cup grated, mild American
  cheese

Mix equal parts of mashed potatoes and flaked fish and form into balls. Put in a greased casserole and pour White Sauce on top. Sprinkle with cheese. Bake in a 350° oven for 20 to 25 minutes or until cheese melts.

Fish Pudding

1-lb. pkg. frozen sole fillets
1 cup White Sauce
  (see *Sauces*)

¼ tsp. salt
2 eggs, separated

Put the fish in 4 cups of salted water and simmer over low heat until tender enough to fall apart; then mix it with the White Sauce and add the salt. Add a small amount of the fish mixture to the beaten egg yolks and mix well. Then stir in the remainder of the fish mixture. Beat the egg whites until stiff and fold them in. Pour the mixture into a greased casserole and set in a pan of hot water. Bake in a 325° oven for 50 minutes, or until done. Serves 4 to 5.

Spaghetti Fish Loaf

2 cups flaked, cooked
  fillet of sole
1 cup cooked spaghetti or rice
2 cups dry bread crumbs

1 cup milk, scalded
2 eggs, separated
⅓ cup half-and-half cream
2 tbsps. melted butter
½ tsp. salt

Soak the bread crumbs in scalded milk. Beat the egg yolks and mix with the crumbs. Add the fish, spaghetti, cream, butter, and salt. Fold in the stiffly beaten egg whites last. Put in a buttered casserole and set in a pan of water. Bake at 325° for 45 to 55 minutes. Serves 4 to 5.

OYSTERS

Creamed Oysters

1 pt. oysters   ¼ tsp. salt
1 tsp. lemon juice   1 cup White Sauce (see *Sauces*)

Add the lemon juice and salt to the White Sauce and blend well. Boil the oysters in their own liquor until the edges curl; then drain. Combine the oysters and sauce and serve on toast. Serves 3 to 4.

Oysters au Gratin

4 cups oysters   4 cups cracker crumbs
2 tbsps. butter   Salt
                   1 pt. milk

Melt the butter and combine with the cracker crumbs and salt. Spread a layer of crumbs in a greased casserole. Add a layer of oysters and their juice. Continue making alternate layers of crumbs and oysters until they have been used up. (Be sure to end with a layer of crumbs on top). Pour milk over all and bake in a 350° oven for 50 to 60 minutes. Serves 5 to 6.

Manhattan Scalloped Oysters

1 cup oysters   ½ cup buttered toast crumbs
1 cup cooked rice   ½ cup grated, mild American
1½ cups Tomato Sauce   cheese
   (see *Sauces*)

In a greased casserole, make alternate layers of rice and oysters, covering each with Tomato Sauce. Sprinkle buttered toast crumbs and cheese over the top. Bake at 400° for 30 to 35 minutes. Serves 3 to 4.

MEAT

Meat is considered an essential part of the diet. The meats usually permitted an ulcer patient are beef, chicken, squab, liver, turkey, and lamb. The amount of meat included on the ulcer diet, however, is strictly the province of the doctor, who is also the proper authority to decide at what stage of the diet meat is permissible.

For the ulcer patient, baking and broiling are the preferred methods of cooking meat. An oven roast should be put on a rack to keep it from cooking in its own juice. Remove all the fat and gristle from meat of any sort before cooking. Chicken livers or sweetbreads should be either boiled or simmered, then combined with a white sauce.

Meats served on the ulcer diet (or used in recipes in this book) must always be scraped, chopped very fine, ground, or put through a blender with the proper amount of liquid.

For recipes using ground meat, it is better to select a lean piece of meat and have it ground "to order," than to buy packaged ground meat. Meat loaf, like roasts, should be baked on a rack.

BEEF

Broiled Steaks

The preferred cuts of steak for broiling are tenderloin, T-bone, club, sirloin, and porterhouse, cut 1 to 2 inches thick.

Lightly grease the broiler pan. Preheat the broiler oven to 550° and place the meat 3 to 4 inches from the heat source. Broil until brown. Season and turn. Brown the other side and season.

To broil steak generally takes from 20 to 45 minutes, depending on the cut of meat. Usually ½ pound of steak should be allowed per serving, but for the ulcer patient the serving should be smaller—according to the doctor's recommendation.

Rump Roast

Remove all fat from the meat and season the roast with salt. Place on a rack in an open roasting pan. Put a small amount of water in the bottom of the pan to keep the drippings from scorching. Bake in a slow (350°) oven for 3 to 4 hours, or until done. Cover the meat with foil or a lid during the last hour of baking. Place a thick slice or half of an onion (permanent ulcer diet) on the rack beside the roast for extra flavor.

In buying roast, usually ½ pound of meat is allowed per person. On the ulcer diet, however, servings are smaller. Consult the patient's physician as to the amount of meat permitted.

GROUND BEEF

Broiled Ground Steak

1 lb. lean ground steak   1 tbsp. butter or margarine
                                     1 tsp. salt

Mix the salt into the ground meat. Shape meat into a round thick patty. Score the top with a knife and pour on melted butter. Broil at 550° with the meat 3 inches from the heat, for 8 to 10 minutes. Turn and score other side. Broil until done. Serves 5.

Steak Patties Pan-Broiled

1 lb. lean ground steak   1 tsp. salt

Mix the salt into the ground meat. Shape into patties about ½ inch thick. Get skillet very hot and sprinkle ½ teaspoon of salt over the skillet bottom. (No shortening is necessary.) Place the patties in the hot skillet and brown quickly. When the under side is browned, turn and brown the other side. Then add 1 or 2 tablespoons water, lower heat, cover, and let simmer 3 or 4 minutes. Serves 5.

Orange–Rice Meat Loaf

1 lb. lean ground steak   1 beaten egg
½ cup orange juice   1 cup cooked rice
                                     ½ tsp. salt

Mix the ingredients together thoroughly and form into a loaf. Bake in a greased casserole in a 350° oven for 1 hour. Serves 6.

Potato Meat Loaf

1 lb. lean ground steak   1 cup seasoned mashed potatoes
½ cup tomato sauce   1 egg
½ tsp. salt   1 tbsp. butter, melted

Mix the ingredients together thoroughly and form into a loaf. Bake in a greased casserole in a 350° oven for 1 hour. Serves 6.

Meat Loaf—Potato Casserole

1 lb. lean ground steak
1 beaten egg
1 cup cornflakes
1 tsp. salt

1 cup buttermilk
6 potatoes, peeled and sliced
⅛ inch thick
1¼ cups boiling water

Mix the ground meat with beaten egg, cornflakes, salt, and buttermilk. In a greased casserole, make alternate layers of thinly sliced raw potatoes and the meat mixture, ending with a layer of meat on top. Pour boiling water over all and cover with foil. Bake in a 350° oven for 2 hours or until potatoes are tender. Serves 6 to 8.

Beef—Lamb Meat Loaf

½ lb. lean ground steak
½ lb. lean ground lamb
1 egg

1 tsp. salt
1 cup milk
1½ cups cornflakes

Mix the ingredients together and form into a loaf. Bake in a greased baking dish in a 350° oven for 1 hour. Serves 6.

Economical Meat Loaf

1 lb. lean ground steak
4 tsps. flour
2 tsps. butter

½ tsp. salt
½ cup cold water

Mix the flour and ground meat. Add melted butter, salt, and cold water, and mix well. Form into a loaf in a greased casserole. Bake 1 hour in a 350° oven. Serves 6.

Meat Loaf with Orange Sauce

1 lb. lean ground steak
1 cup cracker crumbs
1 cup milk

1 beaten egg
½ tsp. salt
⅔ cup Orange Sauce
(see Sauces)

Mix together all the ingredients except the Orange Sauce, and form into a loaf. Bake in a greased casserole in a 350° oven for 1 hour. Pour Orange Sauce over the loaf when serving. Serves 6.

Sour Cream Meat Loaf

1½ lbs. lean ground steak
1 cup sour cream

1½ cups cornflakes
1 tsp. salt
1 beaten egg

Soak the cornflakes in sour cream until soft. Add to the meat, along with the seasoning and egg, and mix well. Put into a greased loaf pan and shape into a loaf. Pour a small amount of water into the pan to keep the juices from burning. Bake in a 350° oven for 1⅓ hours. Serves 6 to 8.

Meat Loaf

1 lb. lean ground steak
1 cup cracker crumbs or
   dry white bread crumbs
1 cup milk

1 egg
1 tsp. onion juice
   (permanent ulcer diet)
1 tsp. salt

Soak the crumbs in milk. Add to the meat, along with the egg, onion juice, and salt. Mix together thoroughly and form into a loaf in a greased loaf pan or casserole. Bake in 350° oven for 1 hour. Serves 6.

Norwegian Meat Loaf

1 lb. steak, ground 4 times
¾ cup cornflake crumbs
2 tbsps. melted butter

2 beaten eggs
3 tbsps. light brown sugar
3 tbsps. lemon juice
1 tsp. salt

Mix the meat with the other ingredients. Shape into a loaf and bake in a greased loaf pan in a 350° oven for 1 hour. Serves 6.

Pineapple Meat Loaf

1 lb. lean ground steak
1 cup pineapple juice

1 cup cornflake crumbs
1 egg
1 tsp. salt

Mix the ingredients together and form into a loaf in a greased casserole. Bake in a 350° oven for 1 hour. Serves 6.

Peach Upside-Down Meat Loaf

1 lb. lean ground steak	1 tsp. salt
No. 303 can Elberta peach halves	1 beaten egg
1 cup dry bread crumbs or cracker crumbs	1 cup milk
	½ cup light brown sugar

1 tbsp. melted butter

Mix the meat with the crumbs, salt, egg, and milk. Put the peach halves in the bottom of a greased casserole, sprinkle the brown sugar over them, and pour melted butter over all. Top with the meat mixture and bake in 350° oven for 1 hour. Serves 6.

LAMB

Broiled Lamp Chops

Have shoulder, rib, or loin chops cut from 1 to 1½ inches in thickness, allowing 1 chop per person. Trim off the fat from the edges. Preheat the broiler to 550° and lightly oil the broiler pan with cooking oil. Place the chops on the rack. Broil 2 to 2½ inches from the heat source until brown on one side. Season, turn, and brown the other side. Season second side with salt and butter. Broiling chops usually takes 15 to 20 minutes.

Roast Leg of Lamb

Remove fat. Season the leg of lamb with salt and place on a rack, skin side down, in a roasting pan. Do not cover; add only a small amount of water. Bake in a slow (325°) oven until tender (meat thermometer should register about 180°). Meat can be covered during the last hour of cooking.

For extra flavor, place half an onion (permanent ulcer diet) on the rack with the lamb. Usually ½ pound of meat is allowed per person, for a normal diet. The ulcer patient should consult his doctor about the amount he is allowed to eat.

Honey-Glazed Lamb Steaks

Lamb steaks, cut from leg of lamb	3 tbsps. lemon juice
¾ cup honey	1 tbsp. orange juice
¼ cup light brown sugar	¼ tsp. salt

Combine honey, brown sugar, the fruit juices, and salt. Cook and stir over low heat until the mixture is well blended. Put the lamb steaks on a rack in a large, open roasting pan. Brush with the honey glaze. Roast in a 350° oven for 1 hour or until done. Baste frequently. (Allow 1 medium-size lamb steak per person.)

Extra-Tender, Moist Lamb Roast

After removing the fat from the lamb, place the meat on a rack in a roasting pan. Sprinkle the meat with salt and place a thick slice of onion on the rack next to it. Put a small amount of water in the bottom of the pan to keep the drippings from burning. Cover the roast with a layer of aluminum foil and put on the roaster cover. Bake in a 275° oven for 7½ hours. (For those who like their roasts browned on top, remove the foil and cover during the last 2 hours.)

LIVER

Broiled Liver

Have 1 pound of baby beef liver cut into slices about ¾ inch thick. Cut off the membrane on the edge of each slice; snip out the veins with scissors. Preheat the broiler to 500°, and butter or oil the broiler pan. Wipe off meat and rub it with vegetable oil or butter. Broil about 5 minutes, with meat 2 to 3 inches from the heat. Then salt, turn, and broil the other side. For the permanent ulcer diet, a slice of onion may be rubbed over the liver to add flavor. Serves 4.

Boiled Chicken Livers

Put ½ pound chicken livers in a saucepan with a small amount of cold water. Simmer until tender. Drain off water, mash the livers, and add salt and butter for seasoning. Serves 3 to 4.

GROUND LIVER

Liver Loaf

1 lb. beef liver	⅓ cup milk
1 cup cornflakes	1 tbsp. lemon juice
2 beaten eggs	1 tsp. salt
	1 tbsp. melted butter

Soak the cornflakes in eggs and milk. Set aside. Cut the membrane from the outside edges of the liver and snip out the veins with scissors. Cook the liver for 5 minutes. Then run through a grinder. Add all the other ingredients to the liver and form into a loaf in a buttered pan. Bake in moderate (350°) oven for 45 to 50 minutes. Serves 6.

Tomato–Liver Loaf

1 lb. beef liver	1 tbsp. lemon juice
1 tbsp. melted butter	1 cup seasoned mashed
1 tsp. salt	potatoes
⅓ cup tomato juice	1 beaten egg

Cook the liver 5 minutes and grind. Add melted butter, salt, tomato juice, lemon juice, mashed potatoes, and beaten egg. Mix well, form into a loaf in a greased loaf pan, and bake in a 350° oven for 1 hour. Serves 6.

Liver–Beef Loaf

½ lb. beef liver, cooked and ground	1 cup milk
½ lb. lean ground steak	1 tsp. salt
1 egg	1 tbsp. melted butter
1 cup cracker crumbs	½ tsp. onion juice (permanent ulcer diet)

Mix all the ingredients together and form into a loaf in a greased casserole dish. Bake in a 350° oven for 1 hour. Serves 6. Serve plain or with Tomato Sauce (see Sauces).

MISCELLANEOUS MEATS

Creamed Sweetbreads

Sweetbreads are quite perishable and so should be precooked before storing in the refrigerator. First, soak them in plenty of cold water for at least 20 minutes. The water should be changed as necessary. Remove any loose membrane. Then cover again with cold water (at least 1 quart), add 1 tablespoon lemon juice and 1 teaspoon salt, and simmer for 15 to 18 minutes. Drain off the water, firm the sweetbreads by plunging them into cold water to cool, and then drain again. Trim off all the tougher membrane and any skin or connective tissue. The sweetbreads can now be stored until needed.

To serve, make White Sauce (see *Sauces*), add the sweetbreads, and stir over low heat until they are hot. Allow ½ to 1 pair of sweetbreads per serving.

Variations: Cooked chicken may be added to creamed sweetbreads. Sweetbreads are also delicious when broiled with butter.

Sweetbreads au Gratin

Precook and clean the sweetbreads as directed in the preceding recipe. Dip them in beaten egg and place in a shallow casserole. Dot with butter; sprinkle toast crumbs and ½ cup of grated cheese over the top. Bake in 350° oven for 25 to 30 minutes.

POULTRY

The white meat of chicken is excellent for the ulcer diet. Frozen chicken breasts can be quickly and simply prepared by placing them on a rack in a roasting pan, adding a little butter and salt, and baking at a low temperature until tender. A whole young chicken weighing about 2½ pounds can be broiled. Have the butcher cut the chicken in half and cut off the wing tips.

Turkey should be roasted at a low temperature to preserve the juices and prevent the meat from drying out.

CHICKEN

Broiled Chicken

Broiling chicken (1–2½ lbs.)   1 tbsp. melted butter
                                          1 tsp. salt

Have the butcher cut the chicken in half. Break the leg and wing joints so that the chicken will lie flat during the broiling process.

Pour the melted butter over the chicken and sprinkle it with salt. Broil at 550°, skin side down, with the rack 5 to 6 inches from the heat, for 10 to 15 minutes. Turn and broil the other side for the same length of time. Continue to turn every 10 or 15 minutes until done. Total time should be 45 to 55 minutes. Serves 2 to 4.

Baked Chicken Breasts

2 large chicken breasts (whole)   2-3 tsps. butter
                                          1 tsp. salt

Wash and clean the chicken breasts. Then place them, skin side up, on a rack in a roasting pan. Dot with butter and sprinkle with salt. Add enough water to cover the bottom of the pan and keep the drippings from burning. Bake in a moderate (350°) oven for 3 hours. After 2 hours, turn the chicken breasts and cover the pan with a lid or aluminum foil. The meat will be tender and moist. Serves 4.

Note: This baking time is for large chicken breasts. For smaller ones, allow less baking time.

Chicken Aristocrat

2 large chicken breasts (whole)   2-3 tsps. butter
                                          1 tsp. salt

Follow the directions for Baked Chicken Breasts (preceding recipe). Serve with Bing Cherry Sauce, made as follows:

No. 303 can dark pitted cherries,   3 tbsps. cornstarch
     strained   3-4 tbsps. lemon juice
3-4 tbsps. sugar   ¾ cup water

Blend the sugar and cornstarch. Add lemon juice, water, and strained cherries and juice. Cook in a double boiler until thick, stirring constantly. (Sauce can be made early and re-heated at serving time.) Serve over chicken breasts after bone and skin have been removed. (Add 1 tablespoon butter for a richer sauce.)

Creamed Chicken Breasts

2 large chicken breasts
 2 cups White Sauce—double batch (see *Sauces*)

Follow the directions for Baked Chicken Breasts. When the chicken is done, allow to cool. Remove the skin, take the meat from the bones, and cut or chop it into small pieces. Combine with the White Sauce, stirring well, and serve over toast points made from day-old white bread.

Variations: For people on the permanent ulcer diet, 1 cup peas and 1 small can mushrooms may be added to the recipe. The creamed mixture may also be served in baked patty shells made by inverting a large muffin tin, shaping day-old bread over the bottom of the cups, and toasting in the oven.

Escalloped Chicken

1 cup cooked chicken (white meat)
 ½ tsp. salt

1½ cups milk
 1 beaten egg

3 tbsps. quick-cooking tapioca
 6 soda crackers, crushed

 1 tbsp. butter

Heat the milk. Add the tapioca and cook in a double boiler about 10 minutes, stirring frequently. Add the chicken, salt, and egg and cook 5 minutes longer. When the mixture starts to thicken, remove from heat and pour into a buttered baking dish. Sprinkle with cracker crumbs and dot with butter. Bake in moderate (350°) oven about 40 minutes. Serves 4 to 5.

Baked Chicken with Sour Cream—Corn Flake Dip

Have a fryer cut into serving-size pieces. After washing and cleaning, dip the pieces into a mixture made up of the following ingredients:

1 cup sour cream   2 tbsps. lemon juice
1 tsp. salt   1 tbsp. sugar

Then roll the pieces of chicken in cornflakes. Put them in a baking pan lined with aluminum foil and cover completely with foil. Bake in a 350° oven about 1½ hours (depending on the size of the fryer). Serves 4 to 5.

Tomato Royale Chicken

1 medium-size frying chicken   1 tbsp. light brown sugar
2 cups tomato juice   1 tbsp. butter
1 tsp. salt   1 tsp. lime juice
    Dash of cinnamon or ½ tsp. onion juice (permanent ulcer diet)

Wash, clean, and cut up the chicken. Arrange the pieces on a rack in a greased baking pan. Mix together all the remaining ingredients and heat until ready to boil. Pour over the chicken. Cover the baking pan with a lid or aluminum foil. Bake 10 minutes in a 400° oven. Lower heat to 350° and bake 55 to 60 minutes longer. Baste once or twice while baking. Serves 4 to 5.

Chicken Loaf

2 cups ground, cooked   1 beaten egg
    chicken   1 cup dry white-bread crumbs
2 cups White Sauce—double   ½ tsp. salt
    batch (see Sauces)   ½ cup cooked peas, strained

Mix the chicken with 1 cup of the White Sauce. Add egg, bread crumbs, and salt. Put in a buttered loaf pan and bake at 350° for 45 to 50 minutes, or until firm. (Set the pan in a dish of hot water to bake.)

Add the strained peas to the second cup of White Sauce and blend well. Serve poured over the chicken loaf. Serves 4 to 5.

Chicken Hash

1 cup chopped, cooked chicken
   or turkey
1 cup cooked rice
1 cup milk

1 tbsp. butter
1 tsp. salt
1 tsp. onion juice
   (permanent ulcer diet)

1 beaten egg

Mix together chicken, rice, milk, butter, and seasoning. Add egg and stir well. Pour into a greased baking dish and bake in a 350° oven for 30 minutes. Serves 4 to 5.

SQUAB

Broiled Squab

Squabs should be cut in half lengthwise. Rub melted butter on the outside of each half. Place, skin side down, on a rack in a broiler pan. Broil 5 to 6 inches from the heat for about 30 minutes, turning once. Allow 1 squab per serving.

Roast Squab

Wash and clean 4 whole squabs for roasting. Stuff them with bread dressing made by mixing together the following ingredients:

1 cup day-old bread crumbs
   (bread may be several days old)
1 tbsp. melted butter
¼ tsp. salt
1 beaten egg

2-3 tbsps. milk
1 tsp. celery juice
   (permanent ulcer diet)
½ tsp. onion juice
   (permanent ulcer diet)

Rub melted butter on the outside of the stuffed squabs. Place them, breast up, on a rack in a roasting pan, and bake at 425° for 10 to 15 minutes. Reduce heat to 325° and continue baking for 35 to 40 minutes. Serves 4.

TURKEY

Roast Turkey

Clean and wash the turkey thoroughly. Rub the cavity with 1 tablespoon of salt. Place turkey, breast side up, on a rack in a baking pan and pour ¼ cup melted butter over it. Put sufficient water in the bottom of the pan to prevent the drippings from scorching. Wrap aluminum foil loosely over the bird. Roast in a 325° oven, basting every 30 to 40 minutes with the pan drippings.

A 10- to 12-pound turkey will take 4 to 5 hours' roasting time. When done, the leg joints should move easily and the meat on the legs should feel soft. Remove the turkey from the pan and let stand a few minutes for easier carving. Serves 8 to 10.

Turkey Spaghetti

2 cups diced, cooked turkey	½ tsp. salt
Half a 7-oz. pkg. spaghetti	1 tbsp. melted butter
2 cups White Sauce—double batch (see *Sauces*)	¾ cup bread crumbs
	1 cup grated, mild American cheese

Cook the spaghetti according to the package directions. Combine the White Sauce with the diced turkey and add salt. Stir in the cooked spaghetti, mix well, and put into a buttered casserole. Mix together the melted butter and bread crumbs and spread on the casserole. Sprinkle the grated cheese over all. Bake in a 350° oven for 25 to 30 minutes. Serves 5 to 6.

Turkey—Rice Ring

2 cups chopped, cooked turkey	½ cup milk
3 cups cooked rice	1 tsp. salt
2 beaten eggs	1 cup White Sauce
½ cup grated, mild American cheese	(see *Sauces*)

Mix cooked rice with beaten eggs, cheese, milk, and seasoning. Bake in a greased ring mold set in a pan of hot water in a 350° oven for 1 hour. Carefully loosen the mixture in the mold and turn it out on a plate. Fill the center with chopped turkey mixed with White Sauce. Serves 5 to 6.

Turkey Egg Wells

2 cups cooked turkey	4 eggs
1 cup White Sauce (see *Sauces*)	½ tsp. salt
½ cup toasted bread crumbs	1½ tsps. butter

Chop the turkey fine or run it through the food chopper. Mix together with the White Sauce and bread crumbs, and then spread in a greased casserole. Make 4 depressions or wells in the surface. Drop a raw egg into each one and season with salt and butter. Bake in a 350° oven until the eggs are set. Serves 4.

Turkey–Cheese Sandwich

Slices of cold, leftover turkey   1 cup grated, mild American cheese
                    1 cup White Sauce (see *Sauces*)

Add the grated cheese to the hot White Sauce and stir until the mixture is smooth. Remove from heat. Toast slices of day-old bread and lay slices of cold turkey on each piece of toast. Pour the cheese sauce on top. Sauce is sufficient for 3 servings.

EGGS

Eggs are easily prepared and provide a quick, nourishing meal at any time of the day. They contain important elements for the maintenance of health, and make a valuable contribution to the ulcer diet, especially in the beginning stages when meat is often restricted. Eggs furnish large amounts of protein as well as iron and certain vitamins. They may be soft-cooked, poached, baked, scrambled, or made into an omelet. Hard-cooked eggs should be reserved for the person on a permanent ulcer diet.

Eggs can be added to the diet in a variety of other ways—combined with fruits, vegetables, or meats, and used in soufflés and various kinds of puddings.

SOFT-COOKED EGGS

Soft-Cooked Eggs

Place eggs in a saucepan in enough cold water to cover them by a half-inch. Heat the water to boiling. Remove from heat, cover, and let stand 3 to 5 minutes, or until the desired consistency is obtained. (One or two trials will show you the correct timing for your preference.)

Coddled Eggs

In a glass or enameled saucepan, heat enough water to cover the eggs. When the water is boiling, turn off the heat and gently drop in the eggs. Leave for 8 to 10 minutes, until of the right consistency.

Poached Eggs

The water for poaching eggs should be barely simmering; it should not boil. An egg-poacher pan will enable beginning cooks to turn out more attractive poached eggs.

Method 1

Grease the poacher cups with butter. Heat the water in the poacher pan to simmering. Break an egg into a saucer, then slide it into a poacher cup. Repeat the process for each egg, and season each with salt and ½ teaspoon butter. Cover the pan and cook about 2 minutes, or until the eggs are of the desired firmness.

Method 2

Put enough salted water into a saucepan to cover the eggs by at least a half-inch. Bring the water to the simmering point. Break an egg into a saucer, then slide it into the simmering water. Repeat the process until the required number of eggs have been added. When a film forms over the yolks and the whites are set, remove the eggs one by one with a slotted spoon and serve on toast points.

SCRAMBLED EGGS

Rice–Egg Scramble

1 cup cooked rice, heated   2 tsps. butter

2 eggs   1 tsp. salt

Melt the butter in a large skillet. Beat the eggs and mix with the rice and salt. Pour the mixture into the skillet. Cook over low heat and stir to prevent burning. Serves 3 to 4.

Scrambled Eggs with Cream

4 eggs   ½ tsp. salt
2 tbsps. cream   1½ tbsps. butter

Beat the eggs with salt and cream. Heat the butter in a skillet. Pour in the egg mixture and cook slowly. When the eggs start to congeal, stir and turn. Serves 5.

Country Scrambled Eggs

2 eggs   ¼ tsp. salt
                            2 tsps. butter

Melt the butter in a skillet. Break the eggs into a saucer, sprinkle with salt, then slide into the skillet. When they start to congeal, stir gently with a fork. Makes 2 to 3 small servings.

Yum-Yum Eggs

2 eggs   ¼ tsp. salt
½ cup milk   2 tsps. butter

Beat eggs, milk, and salt together. Melt the butter in the top of a double boiler, add the egg mixture, and cook 10 to 15 minutes. Do not stir. Remove when the eggs are of custard consistency. Serves 2 to 4.

HARD-COOKED EGGS

Hard-cooked eggs are not as easy to digest as soft-cooked eggs, and therefore are usually reserved for the permanent ulcer diet. The ulcer patient should not eat them during the earlier phases of the ulcer diet unless his physician gives him permission to do so.

Hard-cooked eggs may be added to white sauces for vegetables and used in sandwiches and to garnish salads.

The same method is used for preparing hard-cooked eggs as for soft-cooked eggs, but the eggs should be kept in the water 18 to 20 minutes.

Eggs à la Daisy

2 hard-cooked eggs
  (permanent ulcer diet)

1 cup White Sauce
  (see Sauces)

Dice or slice the whites of the hard-cooked eggs and add them to the hot White Sauce. Pour over toast halves and decorate the top with the sieved yolks. Serves 2 or 3.

Sunflower Eggs

2 hard-cooked eggs
  (permanent ulcer diet)

1 cup grated, mild American cheese
⅓ cup milk

Melt the cheese in the top of a double boiler. Add the milk and stir until smooth. Slice the hard-cooked egg whites and add to the sauce. Serve poured over toast rounds and garnished with the sieved egg yolks. Serves 3 to 4.

BAKED EGG DISHES

Egg Wells in Mashed Potatoes

Prepare mashed potatoes in the usual way and put into a greased casserole. Make 4 wells in the surface and break a raw egg into each. Add salt and a small piece of butter to each egg. Bake in 325° oven for 20 to 25 minutes or until eggs are set. Serves 4.

Egg Casserole

4 eggs
4 tbsps. cream
½ tsp. salt

¾ cup grated, mild American
  cheese
Toast crumbs

2 tsps. butter

Put the eggs and cream in a greased baking dish. Sprinkle salt and grated cheese on top. Then cover with toast crumbs and dot with butter. Bake in slow (325°) oven about 20 to 25 minutes or until eggs are cooked. Serves 4.

Egg Wells in Spinach

10-oz. pkg. frozen spinach
4 eggs
½ tsp. salt

1 cup White Sauce (see *Sauces*)
¾ cup grated, mild American cheese

Cook frozen spinach according to the package directions and strain. Pour into a greased casserole and make 4 wells in the surface. Break an egg into each well and sprinkle it with salt. Cover the top with White Sauce and grated cheese. Bake in a slow (325°) oven for 20 to 25 minutes, or until the eggs are set. Serves 4.

OMELETS

Omelets can be served for breakfast, lunch, or a Sunday night snack. A plain omelet is made by beating together the egg yolks and whites and cooking them on top of the stove. Omelets of the puffy type have the stiffly beaten egg whites folded into the yolks. They are cooked for a few minutes on top of the stove and finished in the oven until the moistness has disappeared.

Plain Omelet

3 eggs
3 tbsps. milk

½ tsp. salt
1 tbsp. butter

Combine the slightly beaten eggs, milk, and salt and stir well. Melt the butter in a heavy skillet and pour in the egg mixture. Cook slowly, lifting the edges of the omelet with a fork or spatula to let the uncooked portion flow underneath. Cook 5 to 8 minutes, or until firm to the touch. (Omelet may be set in a moderate oven to dry the top.) Fold the omelet once and transfer to a hot serving dish. Serves 4.

Variations: Put strained plum or apricot preserves inside the fold and sprinkle the top with confectioners' sugar, or serve with Cheese Sauce (see *Sauces*).

Chicken Liver Omelet

8-oz. pkg. frozen chicken   2 tsps. butter
   livers or ½ lb. fresh livers   2 tsps. lemon juice
             Salt to taste

Bring the chicken livers to a boil and then simmer for 20 to 25 minutes, or until tender. Drain and mash. Add butter, lemon juice, and salt, and mix well.

Make a plain omelet as in the preceding recipe and put the mashed livers inside the fold or on top of the omelet. Serves 4 to 5.

Cheese Omelet

⅓ cup grated, mild American cheese   3 eggs, separated
1 tbsp. milk   2 tbsps. water
½ tsp. salt   2 tbsps. butter

Put the cheese and milk in the top of a double boiler and stir until the cheese melts. Remove from the heat. Add salt and then rapidly stir in the well-beaten egg yolks. Beat the egg whites until foamy. Add the water and beat again until stiff. Fold the cheese-egg yolk mixture into the egg whites.

Melt the butter in a large skillet. Pour in the omelet mixture and cook slowly about 10 minutes—until light brown on the bottom and puffed on top. Transfer skillet to a slow oven (325°) for 8 to 10 minutes until the moistness disappears. Serves 3 to 4.

Top-of-the-Stove Tapioca Omelet

4 eggs, separated   ½ tsp. salt
2 tbsps. quick-cooking   ¾ cup milk
   tapioca   3 tbsps. butter

Combine the tapioca, salt, and milk in a saucepan. Place over medium heat and cook until the mixture comes to a boil, stirring occasionally. Add 1 tablespoon butter. Remove from heat and allow to cool slightly.

Beat the egg whites until stiff. Beat the yolks until thick and lemon-colored. Gradually add the tapioca mixture to the egg yolks and mix well. Fold into the egg whites.

Melt 2 tablespoons butter in a 10-inch skillet. Turn the omelet into the skillet and cook over low heat for 3 minutes. Cover and cook about 10 minutes longer. The omelet is sufficiently cooked when a knife inserted comes out clean. Cut across the omelet at right angles to the handle of the pan, being careful not to cut all the way through. Fold omelet carefully from the handle to the opposite side and lift out onto a hot platter to serve. Serves 5 to 6.

Cornstarch Egg Omelet

3 eggs, separated   1 cup White Sauce (see *Sauces*)
                    2 tbsps. butter

Add the hot White Sauce gradually to the beaten egg yolks, stirring thoroughly after each addition. Fold in the stiffly beaten egg whites. Melt the butter in a large skillet. Pour in the omelet mixture, cover, and cook over low heat until the under side has formed a light brown crust. Test the doneness by lifting the edge of the omelet with a spatula. Finish cooking by putting the omelet in a 300° oven until the surface moistness has disappeared. Serves 4.

SOUFFLÉS

Soufflés are light, puffy mixtures consisting of a basic white sauce with egg yolks, meat, vegetables, or cheese added; stiffly beaten egg whites are folded in last. The same specification for cheese applies to soufflés as to other dishes for the ulcer diet: always use a mild, soft cheese; never use a hard cheese or one with garlic, seeds, or strong flavoring added.

A soufflé should be baked at a low temperature (325°) from 55 to 60 minutes, and served immediately after removing from the oven.

Chicken Soufflé

1½ cups chopped, cooked, white   1 cup White Sauce
    meat of chicken   (see *Sauces*)
3 eggs, separated   ½ tsp. salt

Beat the egg yolks vigorously. Gradually add the White Sauce, stirring well after each addition. Add the chicken and salt, and cool. Fold in the stiffly beaten egg whites last. Pour into an ungreased casserole set in a shallow pan containing an inch of hot water. Bake in a 325° oven for 55 to 60 minutes. Serves 5.

Carrot Soufflé

4-5 medium-size carrots   ½ tsp. salt
3 eggs, separated   1 cup White Sauce
                                 (see *Sauces*)

Cook the carrots according to the directions in the Vegetable Chart; then mash. Beat the egg yolks and add them, along with the salt and mashed carrots, to the White Sauce. Add the stiffly beaten egg whites last. Pour the omelet mixture into an ungreased casserole set in a shallow pan containing an inch of hot water. Bake in a 325° oven for 55 to 60 minutes. Serves 5.

Pea Soufflé

1 cup cooked peas, strained   ½ tsp. salt
2 eggs, separated   ¼ tsp. cream of tartar
1 cup Cheese Sauce
  (see *Sauces*)

Beat the egg yolks. To them, add a small amount of the hot Cheese Sauce and stir rapidly; then combine with the remaining sauce and mix thoroughly. Stir in the peas. Beat the egg whites until foamy; add the cream of tartar and continue to beat until stiff. Fold the beaten whites into mixture and pour into an ungreased casserole set in a shallow pan containing an inch of hot water. Bake at 325° for 55 to 60 minutes. Serves 3 to 4.

Maple Carrot Soufflé

2 cups mashed, cooked carrots   ¼ tsp. salt
4 eggs, separated   ¼ cup light brown sugar
2 cups White Sauce—double   ¼ tsp. cream of tartar
  batch (see *Sauces*)   ¼ tsp. maple flavoring

Beat the egg yolks. Add a small amount of the hot White Sauce and stir rapidly; then combine with the remaining sauce. Stir in the salt, brown sugar, and carrots. Beat the egg whites until foamy; add the cream of tartar and maple flavoring and continue beating until stiff. Fold into the first mixture and pour into an ungreased casserole set in a shallow pan containing an inch of hot water. Bake at 325° for 55 or 60 minutes. Serves 5 or 6.

Corn Soufflé

No. 303 can cream style white   1 cup milk
    corn, strained   1 tbsp. melted butter
3 eggs, separated   1 tbsp. sugar

Cook the strained corn and milk together for approximately 10 minutes. Stir in the butter and sugar. Add a little of the mixture to the beaten egg yolks and mix well. Then combine with the remainder of the hot corn mixture, blending thoroughly. Beat the egg whites until stiff and fold them in. Pour into an ungreased casserole and bake, uncovered, in a 350° oven for 35 minutes. Serves 5.

CHEESE

Cheese is a valuable food on the ulcer diet, supplying a great deal of protein, and also vitamin A and minerals. It can be served in numerous ways—in sandwiches, sauces, casserole dishes, and for dessert.

The person on an ulcer diet is usually restricted to the softer types of cheese, such as cream cheese, cottage cheese, and mild American cheese that is grated and used in casserole dishes. Since cheese is rich, it should be used moderately on the ulcer diet, especially during the beginning stages of the diet.

Cheese Crumb Pudding

¾ cup grated, mild American cheese   Dash of salt
1 cup dry bread crumbs   2 tbsps. butter
1⅓ cups milk   4 eggs, separated

Combine the grated cheese, bread crumbs, milk, salt, and butter in the top of a double boiler and cook until the cheese is melted. Remove from heat. Add a small amount of the hot sauce to the beaten egg yolks, stirring rapidly; then combine with the remaining sauce. Fold the mixture into the stiffly beaten egg whites and pour into an ungreased casserole. Bake in a 325° oven for 55 to 60 minutes. Serves 5.

Cheese Soufflé

¾ cup grated, mild American cheese
3 eggs, separated
3 tbsps. butter

3 tbsps. flour
½ tsp. salt
¾ cup milk

Melt the butter and stir in the flour and salt. Slowly add the milk and cook over low heat until the mixture thickens and is smooth. Add the cheese and cook until it melts, stirring constantly. Beat the egg yolks; to them add a small portion of the hot sauce. Combine with the remaining sauce. Beat the egg whites until stiff and fold them into the mixture. Pour into an ungreased casserole. Make a crown in the cheese mixture by running a knife blade around the pan about an inch from edge. Bake in a 325° oven for 55 to 60 minutes. Serves 4 to 5.

Cottage Cheese Soufflé

1 cup creamed cottage cheese
4 eggs, separated
½ cup cornmeal
1¾ cups milk, heated
½ tsp. salt

1 tbsp. sugar
1 tbsp. butter
1 tsp. onion juice
   (permanent ulcer diet)
¼ tsp. cream of tartar

Apricot preserves, strained

Add the cornmeal to the hot milk. Cook over low heat, stirring constantly until thickened. Add salt and sugar. Beat the egg yolks and gradually add them to the hot mixture, stirring vigorously after each addition. Continue cooking for a few minutes; then remove from stove and add butter, cottage cheese, and onion juice.

Beat the egg whites until foamy; add the cream of tartar and continue beating until stiff. Fold the cornmeal mixture into the egg whites. Pour into an ungreased casserole set in a shallow pan containing an inch of hot water. Bake at 325° for 55 to 60 minutes or until done. Serve with apricot preserves. Serves 5 to 6.

MACARONI, SPAGHETTI, AND NOODLE DISHES WITH CHEESE

Macaroni Loaf

7-oz. pkg. macaroni

1 cup milk

1 cup grated,   2 beaten eggs
  mild American cheese   1 tsp. salt

Cook the macaroni according to the package directions. Combine with the cheese, milk, beaten eggs, and salt. Pour into a greased loaf pan and bake in a 350° oven for 45 minutes. Serves 5.

Macaroni and Cheese No. I

7-oz. pkg. elbow macaroni   2 cups White Sauce—double
¼ lb. mild American cheese,   batch (see *Sauces*)
  grated   ½ tsp. salt

Cook macaroni according to the package directions. Drain in a colander and rinse with cool water. Add salt and grated cheese to the White Sauce and stir until the cheese is melted. Put alternate layers of macaroni and sauce in a greased casserole, and bake in a 350° oven for about 45 minutes. Serves 5.

Macaroni and Cheese No. 2

7-oz. pkg. elbow macaroni   2 tbsps. butter
¼ lb. mild American cheese,   2 cups milk
  sliced thin or grated

Cook macaroni according to the package directions. Drain in a colander and rinse with cool water. Arrange in a greased casserole in layers, topping each layer with slices of cheese, a dash of salt, and bits of butter. Pour the milk over all and bake in a 350° oven about 45 minutes. Serves 5.

Spaghetti and Cheese

Half a 7-oz. pkg. long spaghetti   No. 2 can tomatoes, strained
¼ lb. mild American cheese, grated   1 cup White Sauce
                                         (see *Sauces*)
                    ½ tsp. salt

Cook the spaghetti according to the package directions. Drain in a colander and rinse well. Combine with the strained tomatoes. Add the grated cheese and salt to the White Sauce and stir until smooth. Stir the spaghetti mixture and the cheese sauce together and heat slowly. Serves 5.

Spaghetti Meat Loaf

1 cup cooked spaghetti
(approx. ¼ pkg.)
1 cup ground (or fine-chopped),
cold cooked meat
½ cup grated, mild American
cheese

1 tbsp. butter
1 tbsp. cornstarch
½ tsp. salt
1 cup tomato juice
1 tbsp. lemon juice

Buttered toast crumbs

Cook the spaghetti according to the package directions. Drain in a colander and rinse well. Melt the butter and blend in the cornstarch. Add salt and tomato juice and cook over low heat until thickened, stirring constantly. Add the cooked spaghetti, lemon juice, and meat. Mix well, then put into a buttered casserole and spread the crumbs and grated cheese over the top. Bake in a 350° oven for 30 to 40 minutes. Serves 5.

Hungarian Baked Noodles

Half a 7-oz. pkg. egg noodles
1 tbsp. melted butter
1 cup sour cream
1 tbsp. sugar

½ tsp. onion juice
(permanent ulcer diet)
½ tsp. salt
1 cup grated, mild American
cheese

⅔ cup buttered toast crumbs

Cook the noodles according to the package directions. Put the noodles in a greased casserole and pour butter over them. Combine the sour cream with the sugar, onion juice, and salt, and mix with the noodles. Spread the cheese and toast crumbs over the top. Bake in a 350° oven for 30 minutes. Serves 4 to 5.

Variation: Omit the sour cream, sugar, and onion juice, and use sweet milk.

VEGETABLES

Although vegetables contain large amounts of valuable vitamins and minerals, they often are omitted from the ulcer diet in the beginning. Later, when they are allowed, they should be served frequently.

Vegetables should be thoroughly washed before cooking; a stiff brush is good for this job. Cook in as little water as possible, in order to retain the vitamins and minerals; bring the water to boiling before dropping in the vegetables. Also, whenever you can, utilize the water in which vegetables were cooked.

When vegetables are permitted in the ulcer diet, they should be not only well cooked but also strained. As a person advances to the permanent ulcer diet, he may be allowed certain vegetables unstrained, such as cooked carrots, young beets, spinach, and asparagus. Strongly flavored and rough vegetables like cabbage, turnips, and onions are usually eliminated entirely from the ulcer diet.

WHITE POTATOES

Mashed Potatoes

6 medium-size potatoes

2 tbsps. butter

⅓ cup milk or cream

1 tsp. salt

For cooking potatoes, follow the directions in the Vegetable Chart. Drain well; then mash thoroughly. Add butter, milk, and salt and beat until light and fluffy. Pile in a serving dish, make a crease in the center, and add a pat of butter. Serves 5 to 6.

Potato Balls

4 medium-size potatoes

2 tbsps. butter

1 tsp. salt

Wash and peel the potatoes. With a vegetable scoop, cut into small balls. Cook for 10 to 15 minutes in boiling salted water. Drain. Add butter and salt and gently stir or shake the pan over low heat until the potato balls are coated with butter. Serve hot. Serves 4.

VEGETABLE CHART

VEGETABLE	HOW TO SELECT	HOW TO PREPARE	PRESSURE COOKING	BOILING
Asparagus:				
1 lb. = 2 cups (cut into short lengths)	Choose bright green, crisp stalks with little woody fiber at bottom	Snip off tough lower stalks; wash, and remove scales. Leave whole or cut in 3-inch lengths.	Add ⅔ cup water. Cook 2 to 3 min. after control jiggles.	18 to 20 min. in small amount boiling water, covered or uncovered.
Beets (medium-size, whole):				
1 lb. = 1⅔ cups	Choose smooth, firm beets. Avoid dark red beets with deep ridges.	Snip off tops, leaving 2" of stem; leave root on. Scrub gently with vegetable brush.	Add 1¼ cups water. Cook 20 min. after control jiggles.	Cover with boiling water and cook 30 to 35 min. (young beets). Cover pan.
Carrots (sliced or chunks):				
4-5 medium carrots per lb. 1 lb. serves 4-5	Choose carrots with rich, yellow color. Avoid rough or withered ones.	Wash; then peel or scrape. Slice or cut into chunks.	Add ⅔ cup water. Cook 3 to 4 min. after control jiggles.	Cook covered in small amount boiling water 20 to 22 min.

VEGETABLE	HOW TO SELECT	HOW TO PREPARE	PRESSURE COOKING	BOILING
Cauliflower: 1 med. head serves 5-6	Choose a firm, solid head with no spots or blemishes.	Remove fibrous base and leaves. Wash.	Add 1½ cups water. Cook 7 to 9 min. after control jiggles.	Cover and cook in small amount of boiling water about 28 to 30 min.
Green Beans (or Wax Beans): 1 lb. = 2 cups	Choose well-filled healthy pods that break with a snap. Avoid withered, spotted, or discolored pods.	Wash, snip off ends, and remove strings. Cut in 2- or 3-inch lengths or leave whole.	Add ¾ cup water. Cook 2½ to 3 min. after control jiggles.	Cover and cook in small amount of boiling water about 25 to 33 min.
Lima Beans: 1 lb. = 1 cup (shelled)	Choose well-filled pods. Avoid yellowed or withered ones.	Wash and shell.	Add ¾ cup water. Cook 1 to 2 min. after control jiggles.	Cover and cook in small amount of boiling water about 25 to 33 min.
Peas (garden): 1 lb. shelled = 1¼ cups	Choose bright green, well-filled pods. Avoid shriveled pods.	Shell and wash.	Add ½ cup water and cook 1 to 2 minutes.	Cook in small amount boiling water 15 to 20 min., either covered or uncovered.

VEGETABLE	HOW TO SELECT	HOW TO PREPARE	PRESSURE COOKING	BOILING
Potatoes (white): 4-5 per lb. 1 lb. = 2 cups peeled, diced potatoes	Avoid potatoes with discolorations or soft spots, or a small potato connected to large one.	Wash and peel. Cut into halves.	Add 1½ cups water and cook 8 min.	Cover and cook in small amount boiling water 35 to 40 min.
Potatoes (sweet): 4-5 per lb. 1 lb. serves 4-5	Select firm, bright sweet potatoes without mushy spots or discolorations.	Wash and cut into halves.	Add 1½ cups water and cook 8 min.	Cover and cook in small amount of boiling water 35 to 40 min. Peel after boiling.
Spinach: 1 lb. = 1¾ cups, cooked	Avoid dull, wilted spinach; also leaves with wormholes.	Remove bad leaves and stems. Wash in several waters, lifting spinach out by hand to drain.	Add ⅔ cup water and cook 1½ min.	Cover and cook in small amount of boiling water 10 to 12 min.
Squash (summer): 1 average-size squash makes 1⅓ cups	Select firm, smooth squash, rich yellow in color, without blemishes.	Wash, peel, cut into small pieces.	Add ¾ cup water and cook 2 to 3 min.	Cover and cook in small amount of boiling water 18 to 20 min.

VEGETABLE	HOW TO SELECT	HOW TO PREPARE	PRESSURE COOKING	BOILING
Squash (winter): 1 lb. = 1 cup, cooked	Select firm, smooth, richly colored squash without discolorations.	Wash, cut in halves, remove seeds and stringy portion.	Add 1 cup water and cook 10 to 12 min.	Bake with cut side down 40 to 45 min.
Tomatoes: 4-5 per lb. 1 lb. serves 4-5	Select firm, plump tomatoes. Avoid pale, too soft, or spotted tomatoes.	Wash. Dip quickly in boiling water until skins will slip off. Remove stem scar.	Add ½ cup water and cook 2 to 3 min.	Cover and cook slowly without water for 10 to 15 min.

Potatoes à la Sunflower

4 medium-size white potatoes
1 cup White Sauce
  (see *Sauces*)

2 hard-cooked eggs
  (permanent ulcer diet)
½ tsp. salt

For cooking potatoes, follow the directions in the Vegetable Chart. Chop the egg whites and add to the White Sauce. Drain the cooked potatoes, place in a serving dish, and pour the hot sauce over them. Sprinkle on the salt and sieve the egg yolks over the top before serving. Serves 4 to 5.

Baked White Potatoes

Select potatoes of similar size. Scrub them and remove any bruised spots. Lightly grease the skins; then wrap the potatoes in aluminum foil. Bake in a 400° oven about 1 hour or until tender. Potatoes can also be baked at a lower temperature for a longer period. Allow 1 potato per serving.

Hungarian Baked Potatoes

3 medium-size potatoes
½ cup sour cream
½ cup grated, mild American cheese

½ tsp. salt
½ tsp. onion juice
  (permanent ulcer diet)

Select potatoes of similar size. Scrub them and remove any bruised spots. Lightly grease the skins; then wrap the potatoes in aluminum foil. Bake in a 400° oven about 1 hour or until tender. Remove from oven, cut lengthwise, and scoop out the inside. Mix the cooked potato with sour cream, cheese, salt, and onion juice. Fill the potato shells with this mixture and bake 10 to 15 minutes longer. Serves 3.

Escalloped Potatoes

4 white potatoes
Salt to taste

1½ cups White Sauce
  (see *Sauces*)
2 tsps. butter
1 cup grated, mild American cheese

Wash and peel the potatoes; cook according to the directions in the Vegetable Chart. Cool slightly, slice, and arrange in layers in a greased shallow casserole. Pour part of the White Sauce on each layer. Dot the top layer with butter and sprinkle on salt and the grated cheese. Bake in a 350° oven about 30 minutes, or until the cheese is melted. Serves 4 to 5.

Cottage Cheese Potatoes

5 medium-size potatoes,
  cooked and sliced

2 cups creamed cottage cheese

1 cup White Sauce
  (see *Sauces*)

½ tsp. onion juice
  (permanent ulcer diet)

½ tsp. salt

½ cup grated, mild American
  cheese

Put alternate layers of cooked potatoes, White Sauce with onion juice, and cottage cheese in a greased casserole. Sprinkle salt and grated cheese over the top. Bake in a 350° oven for 30 minutes. Serves 6.

Potato Fluff

1 cup cold mashed potatoes

½ tsp. salt

1 tbsp. melted butter

1 beaten egg

1 cup half-and-half cream

½ cup grated, mild American
  cheese

Beat the potatoes with salt and butter. Add beaten egg plus cream. Beat thoroughly again. Pour into a greased casserole. Sprinkle cheese over the top and bake in a 375° oven for 25 to 30 minutes or until lightly browned. Serves 4.

Mock French Fried Potatoes

5 large potatoes

½ cup milk or cream

2 tsps. butter

½ tsp. salt

⅓ cup grated, mild American
  cheese

½ tsp. onion juice (permanent ulcer diet)

Wash, peel, and prepare potatoes as for French fried potatoes. Put into a greased casserole and pour the milk over them. Add salt and dot with butter. Sprinkle on the onion juice. Cover and bake at 400° for 45 minutes or until potatoes are done. Remove from the oven and sprinkle cheese over the top. Set under the broiler for a minute or two until the cheese melts.

SWEET POTATOES

Baked Sweet Potatoes

Wash sweet potatoes and cut out any bad spots. Wrap potatoes individually in aluminum foil and bake in a 400° oven until tender—usually 30 to

40 minutes. (Sweet potatoes may be baked at a lower temperature when sharing the oven with other vegetables if the baking time is increased. Serve with butter and salt. Allow 1 medium potato per serving.

Duchess Sweet Potatoes

5 cups mashed, cooked, sweet
potatoes
½ cup honey

⅓ cup pineapple juice
¼ tsp. salt
2 tbsps. melted butter

1 tbsp. lemon juice

Combine sweet potatoes with honey, pineapple juice, salt, butter, and lemon juice. Bake in a greased casserole at 350° about 40 minutes. Serves 6.

Sweet Potato Pudding

6 sweet potatoes
2 beaten eggs
½ cup sugar

¼ tsp. lemon extract
½ cup cream
2 tbsps. butter

Cook the sweet potatoes according to the directions in the Vegetable Chart. Mash. Add eggs, sugar, lemon extract, cream, and butter. Bake in a greased casserole in a 350° oven for 30 minutes. Serves 6.

Sweet Potato Orange Cups

4 medium-size sweet potatoes
⅓ cup sugar
1 tbsp. butter
1-2 tbsps. cream

⅛ tsp. salt
⅛ tsp. cinnamon (permanent
ulcer diet)
Marshmallows

Orange shells (scalloped)

Cook the sweet potatoes according to the directions in the Vegetable Chart. Drain and mash. Add sugar, butter, cream, salt, and cinnamon, and beat until smooth. Wash 2 or 3 oranges and cut them in half. Remove the pulp. Cut the edges of the orange halves (or cups) into scallops or points. Fill the cups with the potato mixture, set a marshmallow on top of each, and heat in the oven for a few minutes until the marshmallows brown. Serves 4 to 5.

Sweet Potato Casserole

4 sweet potatoes
2 tbsps. light brown sugar
2 tbsps. cream

Dash of salt
2 tbsps. melted butter
14 marshmallows

Cook the sweet potatoes according to the directions in the Vegetable Chart. Drain and mash. Add the sugar, cream, salt, and butter, and beat until light and fluffy. Put the mixture in a greased casserole. Cover the top with marshmallows. Bake in a 350° oven for 30 minutes. Serves 4 to 5.

Orange Sweet Potatoes

6 medium sweet potatoes

2 tbsps. orange juice

¼ cup boiling water

½ cup light brown sugar

2 tbsps. butter

1 tsp. salt

Cook the sweet potatoes according to the directions in the Vegetable Chart. Drain. Slice in half and arrange the halves in a greased casserole. Mix together the orange juice, boiling water, sugar, butter, and salt; bring to a boil and pour over the potatoes. Bake in a 375° oven for 20 minutes, basting with the syrup. Serves 6.

Variation: Orange extract (¼ teaspoon) may be used instead of orange juice.

Baked Sweet Potatoes and Apples

4 cups cooked, sliced sweet potatoes

3 cups cooked, peeled and sliced apples

¾ cup light brown sugar

¼ tsp. salt

¾ cup water

2 tbsps. butter

Arrange the sweet potatoes and apples in alternate layers in a greased casserole. Sprinkle brown sugar and salt over each layer of apples. Pour on the water and dot the top with butter. Bake in a 350° oven for 30 minutes. Serves 5 to 6.

Yam Marshmallow Balls

No. 303 can yams

¼ cup light brown sugar

1 tsp. melted butter

¼ tsp. vanilla extract

Marshmallows

Vanilla wafer crumbs

Drain the syrup from the yams. Mash yams and add brown sugar, butter, and vanilla extract. Mold the yam mixture around the marshmallows to make small balls. Roll the balls in vanilla wafer crumbs, place on a greased cookie sheet, and set in a 400° oven for a few minutes until the marshmallows melt. Serves 4 to 5.

Baked Candied Sweet Potatoes

5 or 6 medium-size sweet potatoes
2 tbsps. melted butter

3 tbsps. water
⅔ cup sugar

Cook the sweet potatoes according to directions in the Vegetable Chart. Drain, cool slightly, and slice. Arrange the slices in a greased casserole. Mix the remaining ingredients together and bring to a boil. Pour over the sweet potatoes and bake in a 350° oven for 30 to 40 minutes, basting occasionally with the syrup. Serves 5 to 6.

Creamed Sweet Potatoes

4 medium-size sweet potatoes
½ cup light brown sugar
¼ tsp. salt

1 tbsp. lemon juice
1 cup White Sauce
(see *Sauces*)

Cook the sweet potatoes according to the directions in the Vegetable Chart. Drain and put in a greased casserole. Sprinkle with sugar, salt, and lemon juice. Pour White Sauce on top and bake in a 350° oven for 25 minutes. Serves 4 to 5.

SPINACH

Spinach with Cream Cheese Sauce

1½ cups frozen, fresh, or canned
 spinach
1 pkg. cream cheese
 (3 ozs.)

1 egg yolk
¼ tsp. salt
1 tbsp. orange or lemon juice
1 tsp. lime juice

Cook frozen spinach according to the package directions. (For fresh spinach, see the Vegetable Chart.) Strain. Beat the cream cheese and add the egg yolk. Blend until well mixed. Add the salt and citrus juice. Heat in a double boiler or over low heat, stirring frequently. Pour over the hot, cooked spinach. Serves 4 to 5.

Spinach with Sour Cream

1½ cups frozen. fresh, or
    canned spinach
½ tsp. salt

½ cup sour cream
2 tbsps. sugar

Cook frozen spinach according to the package directions. (For fresh spinach, see the Vegetable Chart.) Strain. Add salt, sour cream, and sugar to the hot, cooked spinach. Heat again and serve. Serves 4 to 5.

Creamed Spinach and Eggs

1½ cups frozen, fresh, or canned
    spinach
1 cup White Sauce
    (see *Sauces*)
1 tbsp. butter

1 cup grated, mild American
    cheese
2 hard-cooked eggs
    (permanent ulcer diet)

Cook frozen spinach according to the package directions. (For fresh spinach, see the Vegetable Chart.) Strain. Add butter and arrange in a serving dish or individual casseroles. Add the grated cheese to the hot White Sauce and stir until blended. Then slice the egg whites and add them to the sauce. Pour the sauce over the hot, cooked spinach and garnish the top with sieved egg yolks. Serves 4 to 5.

Sour Cream–Spinach Balls

1¼ cups frozen, fresh, or
    canned spinach
1 cup White Sauce (see
    Sauces), made with sour cream
1 beaten egg
1 cup toasted bread crumbs

½ tsp. salt
½ tsp. onion juice
    (permanent ulcer diet)
1 cup grated, mild American
    cheese

Cook frozen spinach according to the package directions. (For fresh spinach, see the Vegetable Chart.) Strain. Add beaten egg, crumbs, salt, and onion juice. Cool slightly. Form the spinach mixture into 1-inch balls. Put the balls in a greased casserole, pour on the White Sauce, and sprinkle grated cheese over the top. Bake in a moderate oven a few minutes until the sauce bubbles up and the cheese is melted. Serves 4 to 5.

Escalloped Spinach

1½ cups frozen, fresh, or
   canned spinach
½ tsp. salt
½ tsp. onion juice
   (permanent ulcer diet)

½ cup cracker crumbs
1 cup grated, mild American
   cheese
2 tsps. butter

Cook frozen spinach according to the package directions. (For fresh spinach, see the Vegetable Chart.) Strain. Season with salt. Put alternate layers of spinach and cracker crumbs with onion juice in a greased baking dish. Sprinkle grated cheese on top and dot with butter. Bake in a 350° oven for 25 or 30 minutes, or until cheese is melted. Serves 4 to 5.

Spinach–Carrot Mold

2 No. 303 cans spinach
   (permanent ulcer diet)

1 recipe Mashed Carrots
   (see *Vegetables*)

Season the spinach and heat. Then drain and arrange in a greased ring mold. Unmold on a serving dish and fill the center with hot Mashed Carrots. Garnish with hard-cooked egg slices (permanent ulcer diet). Serves 6 to 8.

BEETS

Boiled Beets

Cook beets according to the directions in the Vegetable Chart. When they are tender, remove the skin and stems, and slice or dice. Serve with butter and a little salt for seasoning. Beets should be strained for the beginning phases of the ulcer diet. Allow 1 bunch (4 medium beets) for 4 servings.

Creamed Beets

2 cups small cooked beets, left
   whole (permanent ulcer diet)
1½ cups White Sauce
   (see *Sauces*)

2 tbsps. orange juice
½ tsp. salt

Mix the beets with the White Sauce. Add the orange juice and salt and heat before serving. Serves 5 to 6.

Beets in Orange Sauce

2 cups fresh or canned beets
1 cup sour cream

3 tbsps. orange juice
¼ tsp. salt

Cook fresh beets according to the directions in the Vegetable Chart. Drain. Remove skin and stems from the beets; then strain. Add sour cream, orange juice, and salt. Cook over low heat for a few minutes and serve hot. Serves 4 to 5.

Dried Apricot—Cream Beets

2 cups canned beets, strained
2 cups cooked dried apricots, strained
1-2 tbsps. strained honey

½ cup sugar
2 tbsps. orange juice
1 cup sour cream
Dash of salt

Combine the beets with all the other ingredients. Cook over low heat for a few minutes and serve hot. Serves 5 to 6.

Harvard Beets

2 cups canned beets
1 tbsp. butter
1 tbsp. cornstarch

2-3 tbsps. sugar
¼ tsp. salt
¼ cup lemon juice

Drain the juice from the beets and reserve. Strain the beets. Melt the butter, add the cornstarch, sugar, and salt, and blend well. Add the lemon juice and beet juice gradually and cook until thick. Then add the beets and heat again. Serves 5 to 6.

GREEN BEANS

Green String Beans or Wax Beans

2 cups frozen, fresh, or canned green beans or wax beans

¼ cup lemon juice
1 tbsp. butter
¼ tsp. salt

Cook frozen beans according to the package directions. (For fresh beans, see the Vegetable Chart.) Strain. Mix together the lemon juice, butter, and salt and bring to a boil. Pour over the hot beans. Serves 5 to 6. (A smaller amount of lemon juice may be used.)

Creamed Green Beans

2 cups frozen, fresh, or canned
green beans
1 cup White Sauce
(see *Sauces*)

2 tsps. lemon juice
½ tsp. salt

Cook frozen green beans according to the package directions. (For fresh beans, see the Vegetable Chart.) Strain. Add the lemon juice and salt slowly to the White Sauce. Then stir in the strained green beans. Serve heated. Serves 4 to 5.

Variation: Hard-cooked egg slices may be added to the White Sauce for the permanent ulcer diet.

Green Beans with Sour Cream

4 cups fresh green beans
1 cup White Sauce, made with sour
cream instead of milk (see *Sauces*)
1 tsp. salt

2 tsps. sugar
1 cup grated, mild American
cheese
½ cup cornflake crumbs

1 tbsp. melted butter

Cook the green beans according to the directions in the Vegetable Chart. Drain off the juice and strain the beans. Add salt, sugar, and green beans to the hot White Sauce. Pour into a greased 1½-quart casserole. Sprinkle cheese over the top. Combine the cornflake crumbs with butter and sprinkle them over the cheese. Bake in hot (400°) oven for 20 minutes. Serves 6 to 8.

PEAS

Buttered Peas

1½ cups frozen, fresh, or
canned peas

1 tsp. sugar
2 tsps. butter
¼ tsp. salt

Cook frozen peas according to the package directions. (For fresh peas, see the Vegetable Chart.) Strain. Add sugar, butter, and salt. Serve heated. Serves 4 to 5.

Creamed Peas

1½ cups frozen, fresh, or   ¼ tsp. salt
   canned peas   1 cup White Sauce
1 tsp. sugar   (see *Sauces*)

Cook frozen peas according to the package directions. (For fresh peas, see the Vegetable Chart.) Strain. Add the sugar and salt to the hot White Sauce. Then add strained peas. Serve heated. Serves 4 to 5.

Pea—Carrot Loaf

1½ cups fresh, frozen, or   ½ tsp. salt
   canned peas   1 tbsp. sugar
½ cup mashed, cooked carrots   ½ tsp. onion juice
1 cup cornflake crumbs   (permanent ulcer diet)
2 tsps. lemon juice   ½ cup finely cut head lettuce
½ cup milk   (permanent ulcer diet)
1 beaten egg   ½ cup grated, mild American
2 tsps. melted butter   cheese

Cook frozen peas according to the package directions. (For fresh peas, see the Vegetable Chart.) Leave the peas unstrained for the permanent ulcer diet. Drain.

Mix the peas with all the other ingredients except the cheese. Put into a greased casserole and form into a loaf. Sprinkle the grated cheese over the top. Bake 30 to 40 minutes at 350°. Serves 5 to 6.

TOMATOES

Creamed Tomatoes

No. 2 can tomatoes, strained   1 tbsp. cornstarch
1 tbsp. butter   2-3 tbsps. sugar
                                ¼ tsp. salt

Melt the butter; stir in the cornstarch, sugar, and salt. Cook over low heat until smooth, stirring constantly. Slowly add the strained tomatoes and cook for a few minutes more, until thickened. Serves 5 to 6.

Tomato Pudding

2 cups fresh or canned
  tomatoes
3 tbsps. sugar

¼ tsp. salt
2 pieces of crumbled toast
1 tbsp. butter

Cook fresh tomatoes according to the directions in the Vegetable Chart. Strain the tomatoes. Pour into a greased casserole, sprinkle on the sugar and salt, and put toast crumbs on the top. Pour melted butter over all. Bake in a moderate (350°) oven for 20 minutes. (Grated cheese may also be sprinkled over the top.) Serves 4 to 5.

Stewed Fresh Tomatoes

4 large tomatoes, peeled
2 tsps. butter
¼ tsp. salt

2 tsps. sugar
½ tsp. onion juice
  (permanent ulcer diet)

Cut the tomatoes into small pieces and put in a saucepan. Cook over low heat for a few minutes until the tomatoes are tender. Add butter, salt, sugar, and onion juice. Run through the vegetable strainer, reheat, and serve. (Do not add water.) Serves 4.

Tomato—Rice—Cheese Casserole

1 cup cooked rice
½ cup strained tomatoes
½ cup cubed, mild American
  cheese

1 cup White Sauce
  (see *Sauces*)
1 tbsp. butter
¼ cup soda cracker crumbs

½ tsp. salt

Spread alternate layers of rice, tomatoes, and cheese in a greased casserole. Pour White Sauce over the top. Melt the butter and stir together with the cracker crumbs and salt. Sprinkle the buttered crumbs on top of the vegetable mixture. Bake in a moderate (350°) oven for 25 minutes.

CORN

Creamed Corn

No. 303 can strained
  cream style corn
1 tbsp. sugar

Dash of salt
1 cup White Sauce
  (see *Sauces*)

Add sugar, salt, and strained corn to the hot White Sauce. Heat again and serve. Serves 5 to 6.

Corn Casserole

No. 303 can cream style corn,
strained
1 beaten egg
1 tbsp. sugar
¼ tsp. salt

1 cup dry bread crumbs
½ cup milk
2 tsps. butter
½ cup grated, mild American
cheese

Add the egg, sugar, salt, bread crumbs, and milk to the strained corn. Mix well and pour into a buttered casserole. Put butter and cheese on the top and bake in a 350° oven for 30 minutes. Serves 5 to 6.

Fresh Corn Pudding

6 ears of fresh corn
2 eggs
2 tbsps. sugar

½ cup milk
¼ tsp. salt
1 tbsp. butter

Remove corn husks. Wash the corn and slit the kernels lengthwise with a sharp knife. Scrape out the milk and pulp into a bowl. Put the corn, eggs, sugar, milk, salt, and butter into blender (divide into two parts if the blender is small). Blend for few minutes at high speed, until smooth. Pour into a greased casserole and bake at 350° for 40 to 45 minutes. Serves 4 to 5.

LIMA BEANS

Creamed Buttermilk Limas

10-oz. pkg. frozen lima beans,
cooked and strained
1 cup White Sauce, made with
buttermilk (see *Sauces*)

1 egg yolk
½ tsp. salt
1 tbsp. lemon juice

Add the egg yolk, salt, and lemon juice to the White Sauce, stirring vigorously. Stir in the strained lima beans. Serve heated. Serves 4 to 6.

Buttered Lima Beans

1½ cups strained, cooked   2 tsps. butter
  lima beans   ½ tsp. salt

Add butter and salt to the strained beans and heat. Serves 4 to 5.

Lima Beans—Mashed Potatoes

Prepare mashed potatoes the usual way. Spread in a greased casserole and make 4 wells in the potatoes. Fill the wells with strained, cooked, green lima beans that have been seasoned with butter and salt. Sprinkle the top with grated, mild American cheese and bake in a 350° oven about 25 minutes. Serves 4.

Baked Lima Bean Loaf

1 pkg. frozen lima beans, cooked,   1 tsp. onion juice
  drained, and strained   (permanent ulcer diet)
1 beaten egg   ½ cup soda cracker crumbs
2 tbsps. light brown sugar   ½ cup cornflake crumbs
½ cup milk or tomato juice   2 tsps. melted butter
1 tbsp. lemon juice   ½ cup chopped head lettuce
      ½ cup grated, mild American cheese

Mix all the ingredients except the cheese together and form into a loaf in a greased casserole. Sprinkle the cheese over the top. Bake in a 350° oven for 30 to 40 minutes. Serves 5.

ASPARAGUS

Buttered Asparagus

2 cups fresh asparagus   ¼ tsp. salt
      2 tsps. butter

Cook fresh asparagus according to the directions in the Vegetable Chart. Strain. Add salt and butter and serve heated. Serves 4 to 5.

Escalloped Asparagus

2 cups strained, cooked   1 cup White Sauce
  asparagus   (see Sauces)
1 cup soda cracker crumbs   ¾ cup grated, mild American
      cheese

Arrange alternate layers of seasoned asparagus, cracker crumbs, and White Sauce in a baking dish. Sprinkle cheese over the top and bake in a 350° oven until the cheese is melted, about 20 to 25 minutes. Serves 4 to 6.

Creamed Asparagus with Eggs

10-oz. pkg. frozen asparagus
1 cup White Sauce
 (see Sauces)

½ tsp. salt
2 hard-cooked eggs, sliced
 (permanent ulcer diet)

Cook frozen asparagus according to the package directions. Strain. Add salt, White Sauce, and hard-cooked egg slices. Serve on toast points. Serves 4 to 6.

Asparagus with Hollandaise Sauce

1 lb. fresh asparagus

1 tbsp. butter
½ tsp. salt

Cook fresh asparagus according to the directions in the Vegetable Chart. Add butter and salt. Put into a serving dish and pour hot Hollandaise Sauce (see Sauces) on top. Serves 4 to 5.

CAULIFLOWER

Buttered Cauliflower

1 medium head of cauliflower
 (permanent ulcer diet)
1 tsp. salt

1 tbsp. melted butter
½ cup grated, mild American
 cheese

Cook cauliflower according to the directions in the Vegetable Chart and drain. Arrange in a serving dish and sprinkle with salt. Pour on the butter and sprinkle the cheese over the top. Serves 5.

Creamed Cauliflower

1 medium head of cauliflower
 (permanent ulcer diet)

1 cup White Sauce
 (see Sauces)
1 tsp. salt

Cook cauliflower according to the directions in the Vegetable Chart and drain. Arrange in a serving dish and sprinkle with salt. Pour White Sauce over the top. (Cheese Sauce may be used instead.) Serves 5.

CARROTS

Maple-Glazed Carrots

4 medium carrots, sliced or cut in chunks (permanent ulcer diet)

¼ cup light brown sugar

1 tbsp. butter

¼ tsp. salt

¼ cup water

¼ tsp. maple flavoring

Wash and scrape the carrots. Using the tines of a fork, make deep ridges in the sides of the carrots before slicing them. Cook according to the directions in the Vegetable Chart. Drain. Bring sugar, butter, salt, and water to a boil and simmer for 5 minutes. Add maple flavoring. Put the cooked carrot slices in a greased casserole and pour the hot syrup over them. Basting once or twice, bake in a 375° oven for 20 to 25 minutes. Serves 4 to 5.

Mashed Carrot—Potatoes

4 medium-size carrots, cooked and mashed

4 medium-size potatoes, cooked and mashed

1 tbsp. butter

1 tsp. salt

½ tsp. onion juice (permanent ulcer diet)

½ cup milk

Combine the mashed carrots and potatoes. Add butter, salt, onion juice, and milk, and beat until smooth. Serve hot. Serves 4 to 5.

Honey—Orange Carrots

1 bunch carrots, sliced or cut in chunks (permanent ulcer diet)

⅓ cup strained fresh orange juice

1 tbsp. butter

¼ cup strained honey

Cook the carrots according to the directions in the Vegetable Chart. Drain. Mix the orange juice, butter, and honey together. Heat until the butter is melted. Pour the hot mixture over the carrots. Serves 4 to 5.

Mashed Carrots

Cook carrots according to the directions in the Vegetable Chart. Drain and strain. Add cream, salt, and butter and beat until the carrots have the consistency of mashed potatoes. If desired, add 1 or 2 teaspoons sugar.

European Carrots

1 bunch carrots   ⅔ cup light brown sugar
  (permanent ulcer diet)   2 tbsps. butter
2½ tbsps. lemon juice

Wash and scrape the carrots; then cut into 2-inch sticks about ⅛ inch in thickness. Cook in boiling water until tender; drain. Mix lemon juice, sugar, and butter and bring to a boil. Pour over the carrot sticks. Serve hot. Serves 4 to 5.

SQUASH

Squash

1½ lbs. yellow (summer) squash   2 tsps. butter
                                      ¼ tsp. salt

Cook squash according to the directions in the Vegetable Chart. Strain. Add butter and salt. Serves 3 to 4.

Frozen Squash

10-oz. pkg. frozen squash   2 tsps. butter
1 tbsp. light brown sugar   ¼ tsp. salt

Put all ingredients in the top of a double boiler and cook until the squash is smooth, stirring occasionally. Serves 4 to 5.
Variation: In place of brown sugar, use 2 tablespoons of marshmallow creme.

Delicious Acorn Squash

2 medium-size acorn squash   ¼ tsp. salt
2 tbsps. light brown sugar   3 tsps. butter

Wash squash, cut into halves, and remove seeds. Grease cavities lightly with butter and place on a greased cookie sheet with the cut side down. Bake in a 400° oven for 35 to 40 minutes or until tender when pierced with a fork. Remove from oven and allow to cool for few minutes. Scrape out the squash pulp with a spoon. Add brown sugar, salt, and butter to the pulp and mix well. Heat slowly. Serves 4.

Acorn Squash Casserole

Wash squash, cut into halves, and remove seeds and stringy portion. Place in a greased casserole, cut side down, and bake at 350° for 35 minutes. Then turn squash over and put 2 teaspoons light brown sugar and 1 teaspoon butter in each cavity. Sprinkle ¼ teaspoon salt over the top. Continue baking for another 30 minutes at the same temperature.

Variation: Put 2 or 3 teaspoons honey, 1 teaspoon orange juice, and 1 teaspoon butter in each squash cavity.

Squash with Cherry Wells

10-oz. pkg. frozen squash
¼ cup light brown sugar
2 tsps. butter

¼ tsp. salt
1 recipe Cherry Sauce
(see *Sauces*)

Cook squash with sugar, butter, and salt in the top of a double boiler until smooth. Transfer to a greased casserole and make 4 or 5 wells in the surface. Spoon hot Cherry Sauce into the wells and heat in a 350° oven for a few minutes. Serves 4 to 5.

Squash Fluff Pudding

10-oz. pkg. frozen squash
¼ tsp. salt

2 tsps. butter
8 diced marshmallows

Cook squash, covered, along with the other ingredients, in the top of a double boiler until smooth, stirring occasionally. Serves 5.

MISCELLANEOUS VEGETABLES

Vegetable Medley

2 pkgs. frozen green peas and
   carrots, cooked but unstrained
   (permanent ulcer diet)
1 cup cooked, cubed potatoes
1½ cups White Sauce
   (see *Sauces*)

1 tsp. onion juice
   (permanent ulcer diet)
½ tsp. salt
2 tsps. sugar

Add onion juice, salt, and sugar to the White Sauce. Then add the cooked vegetables and cook over low heat until the mixture is hot. Serves 6.

BREADS

The breads usually recommended for the ulcer diet are Melba toast, day-old white bread, and rusk, a bought, prepared toast that is palatable as well as nutritious.

Hot breads, whole-wheat breads, or breads with seeds are usually eliminated from the ulcer diet; pancakes, waffles, and doughnuts are also generally forbidden.

TOAST

Melba Toast

Place thin slices of day-old bread in a long, flat pan in a slow oven (300°). Bake until bread is light brown in color and dry and crisp. Store in airtight containers.

Milk Toast

3 slices day-old white bread
2 cups milk

1 tbsp. butter
¼ tsp. salt

Toast the bread, cut into cubes, and place in a serving dish. Add butter and salt to the milk and heat to the boiling point. Pour over bread cubes and serve while hot. Serves 2 to 3.

SANDWICHES

Sandwiches can be used for many different occasions—packed in a lunch box or picnic basket, served for lunch, for afternoon and evening parties, after the theater, and also for a Sunday-night snack.

Sandwiches can be made well ahead of serving time and stored in a large crock or other suitable container. Cover the sandwiches with a piece of heavy waxed paper and put a cloth wrung out of cold water over the paper. They will stay fresh for several hours. Sandwiches can also be put in a freezer container (cover each layer with foil) and frozen for later use.

There is an almost endless variety of sandwich spreads and fillings to choose from, as well as several different types of sandwiches—the open-face sandwich, the closed one, the dainty tea sandwich cut into fancy shapes, the individual frosted loaf sandwich, and the frosted whole loaf cut into slices.

These sandwich filling suggestions are easily prepared and can be used for the everyday occasion on the ulcer diet:

1. Cooked chicken livers, or cooked calf's liver, ground and then mixed with home-made salad dressing, a few drops of onion juice (permanent ulcer diet), hard-cooked eggs (permanent ulcer diet), 2 teaspoons lemon juice, and a few crushed soda crackers. (Serve on toasted rounds of day-old bread.)

2. Boiled halibut mixed with Homemade Salad Dressing (see *Index*), hard-cooked eggs (permanent ulcer diet), lemon juice, and crushed soda crackers.

3. Slices of mild, soft American cheese. (Serve on buttered pieces of day-old bread.)

4. Slices of hard-cooked egg (permanent ulcer diet) on finely chopped head lettuce. (Serve on toasted bread.)

5. Cream cheese, softened, beaten, and thinned with orange juice. (Serve on toasted bread.)

6. Cream cheese, softened, beaten, and thinned with pineapple juice. (Serve on toasted bread.)

7. Minced cold chicken, roast beef, or turkey moistened with a bit of Homemade Salad Dressing (see *Index*).

8. Jelly, whipped to smooth consistency and mixed with cream cheese. (Serve on buttered rounds of day-old bread.)

9. Butter creamed with a little lemon or orange juice, then mixed with an equal amount of honey. (Serve on hot, toasted day-old bread, or crackers.)

10. Sliced ripe bananas on finely chopped head lettuce (permanent ulcer diet) with a bit of Homemade Salad Dressing (see *Index*). (Serve on plain day-old bread.)

FANCY SANDWICHES

The bread used to make sandwiches for teas and parties can be cut into interesting shapes either freehand or by using cookie cutters. These fancy sandwiches can be garnished on top with bits of hard-cooked egg (permanent ulcer diet), or the hard-cooked yolk can be grated and arranged on top of the sandwich to represent a flower center and pieces of the egg white used to represent the flower petals. Cream cheese can be used to make fancy swirls and designs on the tops of sandwiches.

Party sandwiches should be served on attractive trays, so that they are eye-catching as well as appealing to the palate.

Jelly-Roll Sandwich

Cut the top crust from a loaf of unsliced day-old bread, lengthwise. Cut the bread into 4 even, lengthwise slices. Spread each slice with softened butter and firm jelly that has been whipped. Then roll each slice as for a jelly roll. Wrap in waxed paper and chill. Cut in slices to serve.

Frosted Jelly Sandwich Loaf

Cut the top crust from a loaf of unsliced day-old bread. Cut the bread into 4 even, lengthwise slices. Spread the first slice with softened butter, the second slice with butter and firm jelly. Place second slice, jelly side down, on the buttered slice. Repeat the process until all but the top and bottom of the loaf have been spread. Cover the loaf with a lightly moistened cloth and wrap in waxed paper. Chill for 4 to 5 hours. Then unwrap the loaf and place it horizontally on a serving plate. Frost the entire loaf with tinted cream cheese that has been mixed with cream and jelly. The top of loaf may be decorated with cream cheese tinted a contrasting color. Chill again and slice when ready for serving.

Variations: Use egg salad, meat salad, or fish salad for the filling.

Individual Sandwich Loaf

Take individual slices of bread and cut each into three pieces. Spread butter and jelly on each piece and stack. Frost these small loaves the same as in the preceding recipe and decorate if desired. Chill until ready to serve.

DESSERTS

A person on the ulcer diet is often confined to simple desserts in the beginning—egg custards, tapioca or cornstarch puddings, and gelatin desserts. The eggs in the custards and some of the puddings help to supply the needed protein that is missing in the earlier stages of an ulcer diet when meat is omitted.

The monotony of such frequent serving of puddings and custards can be overcome somewhat by varying the flavorings. Besides the usual vanilla, there are maple, pineapple, orange, rum, lemon, banana, and almond extracts to add variety.

Desserts should be attractive as well as nutritious. A dessert mixture can be tinted with a few drops of vegetable coloring, and the top can be decorated with swirls or rosettes of whipped cream or artistically arranged lemon and orange slices.

All fruit desserts for the ulcer diet should be made of cooked and strained fruit, with the exception of banana dishes. Later, on the permanent ulcer diet, it may not be necessary to strain some of the softer fruits, but always check with the doctor first. However, fruit skins and seeds should always be removed.

Frozen desserts are easily prepared and are particularly appealing in hot weather. Some of these are made with a cooked custard base, some with an uncooked custard. As a rule, those made with cooked custard are smoother.

For an ulcer patient, frozen desserts should be removed from the refrigerator a short time before serving, so that they are not too cold; they should be eaten slowly and allowed to warm in the mouth before being swallowed. The ulcer patient should, in fact, beware of extremes of temperature in all foods.

CUSTARDS

Boiled Custard

4 beaten eggs

½ cup sugar

¼ tsp. salt

2 tsps. cornstarch

4 cups milk

1 tsp. vanilla extract

Mix the sugar, salt, and cornstarch. Gradually add the milk and beaten eggs. Cook in a double boiler about 15 minutes, stirring constantly, until the custard coats the spoon and starts to thicken. Cool before adding the vanilla. Serves 5 to 6.

Fancy Boiled Custard

4 eggs

⅓ cup sugar

2 cups milk, heated

¼ tsp. salt

1 tsp. vanilla extract

1 cup cream, whipped and
   sweetened with 1 tbsp. sugar

8-10 lemon wafers, crushed

Beat the eggs; then add the sugar, heated milk, and salt. Cook in a double boiler until the mixture coats the spoon, stirring constantly. Cool, and then add vanilla and whipped cream. Sprinkle the wafer crumbs on the top. Serves 5.

Orange Custard

4 egg yolks
⅔ cup sugar
¼ tsp. salt

1 tbsp. cornstarch
⅔ cup orange juice
1¼ cups cream

¼ cup cream, whipped

Mix the sugar, salt, and cornstarch. Add the egg yolks and stir well. Blend in the orange juice and 1¼ cups of cream. Cook in the top of a double boiler until thickened, stirring constantly. Cool before folding in the whipped cream. Serve as dessert or a dessert topping. Serves 4.

Butterscotch Custard

4 beaten eggs
½ cup light brown sugar
¼ tsp. salt
2 tsps. cornstarch

4 cups scalded milk
1 tsp. vanilla extract or ¼ tsp.
  maple flavoring

Mix the brown sugar, salt, and cornstarch. Add a small amount of the milk to make a paste. Stir in the eggs and the remaining milk. Cook in the top of a double boiler until thickened, stirring constantly. Cool. Add the vanilla or maple flavoring. Serves 4 to 5.

Cocoa—Rice Custard

2 eggs, separated
½ cup sugar
½ tsp. salt

1 tbsp. cocoa
2 cups cooked rice
2 cups milk, heated

1 tsp. vanilla extract

Mix the sugar, salt, cocoa, and rice together. Stir in the egg yolks and mix well. Add the heated milk and cook in a double boiler until thickened, stirring constantly. Remove from the stove and add the vanilla. Beat the egg whites until stiff and fold them in last. Serve with whipped cream. Serves 4 to 5.

Baked Custard

4 beaten eggs
½ cup sugar

¼ tsp. salt
3 cups milk, scalded

1 tsp. vanilla or rum extract

Combine the beaten eggs with sugar and salt. Gradually add the scalded milk and flavoring. Pour into a large baking dish and set the dish in a pan containing hot water that comes up to the height of the custard. Bake at 350° for 45 to 50 minutes or until done. Test by inserting a knife into the center and side. If it comes out clean, the custard is done. Serves 4 to 5.

Lemon Cup Custard Pudding

2 eggs, separated	⅔ cup sugar
3 tbsps. lemon juice	3 tbsps. butter or margarine
2 heaping tsps. flour	1 cup milk

Cream together the flour, sugar, and butter. Add the egg yolks and mix well. Then slowly add the milk and lemon juice. Beat the egg whites until stiff and fold into the mixture. Pour into greased custard cups, set in a pan of hot water, and bake in slow (325°) oven for 45 minutes. Serves 4.

TOP–OF–THE–STOVE PUDDINGS

Plain Tapioca Pudding

3 beaten eggs	¼ tsp. salt
½ cup sugar	5 cups milk
4 tbsps. quick-cooking tapioca	1 tsp. vanilla extract

Mix the beaten eggs with the sugar, tapioca, salt, and milk in a saucepan. Cook over medium heat, stirring constantly, until the mixture comes to a full boil and begins to thicken—6 to 8 minutes. Remove from heat and add vanilla. Cool. Serves 5 to 6.

Variations: Sliced bananas, apricot puree, cubes of cranberry jelly, strained peaches, applesauce, or cubes of gelatin in assorted colors may be added to the cooled pudding.

Lemon Tapioca Pudding

2 tbsps. lemon juice	⅛ tsp. salt
¼ cup quick-cooking tapioca	2 cups boiling water
½ cup sugar	1 cup cream, whipped

Put all the ingredients in a saucepan with the exception of the whipped cream, and bring to a boil over direct heat, stirring constantly. Cool, and add the whipped cream. Serves 4.

Tapioca Fluff Pudding

3 eggs, separated
½ cup sugar
¼ tsp. salt

4 tbsps. quick-cooking tapioca
4 cups milk
½ tsp. lemon extract
½ tsp. vanilla extract

Beat the egg whites until they form soft peaks, and stir in ¼ cup of sugar. Set aside. Then put the remaining ¼ cup sugar, the salt, egg yolks, tapioca, and milk in a saucepan and cook over medium heat, stirring until the mixture comes to a full boil—6 to 8 minutes. Remove from heat and slowly add the hot mixture to the beaten egg whites. Blend well. Cool and add vanilla and lemon extracts. Serves 6 to 8.

Pineapple Tapioca Sponge Pudding

1 cup pineapple juice
½ cup sugar
3 tbsps. quick-cooking tapioca

1 beaten egg
2 cups milk, scalded
¼ tsp. lemon extract
Slices of stale sponge cake

Add the sugar, tapioca, egg and pineapple juice to the scalded milk. Cook over low heat, stirring constantly until the mixture begins to thicken. Then cool and add flavoring. Line sherbet glasses with slices of stale sponge cake. Pour the pudding over the cake and garnish with whipped cream. Serves 3 to 4.

Banana Tapioca

2 bananas
5 tbsps. quick-cooking tapioca
2 eggs, separated

½ cup sugar
Dash of salt
4½ cups milk
3 tbsps. lemon juice

Mix the tapioca, egg yolks, sugar, salt, and milk in a saucepan. Cook over low heat until thickened, stirring constantly. Then cool. Slice the bananas and pour lemon juice over them. Add to the tapioca mixture. Beat the egg whites until stiff and fold them in last. Chill and serve in sherbet glasses. Serves 4 to 5.

Pineapple Tapioca

¼ cup quick-cooking tapioca
2½ cups pineapple juice

⅛ tsp. salt
½ cup sugar

Mix all the ingredients together and boil over medium heat until the mixture starts to thicken, stirring constantly. Remove from heat and cool. If desired, ¼ teaspoon lemon extract may be added. Serves 3 to 4.

Grape Tapioca

¾ cup grape juice
¼ cup quick-cooking tapioca
1¾ cups water

½ cup sugar
1 tbsp. lemon juice
Dash of salt

Combine all the ingredients in a saucepan and bring to a boil over direct heat, stirring constantly—6 to 8 minutes. Serves 4.

Rhubarb Tapioca

2½ cups rhubarb, cut in small pieces
⅓ cup quick-cooking tapioca
⅔ cup sugar

Dash of salt
2½ cups boiling water
½ cup cream, whipped

Add the rhubarb, tapioca, sugar and salt to the boiling water. Cook over low heat or in a double boiler about 25 minutes, or until the rhubarb is soft. Stir often. When done, remove from the stove and chill. Serve with dabs of whipped cream on top. Serves 4 to 5.

Cornstarch Pudding

3 tbsps. cornstarch
⅓ cup light brown sugar
¼ tsp. salt

2 cups milk
1 tsp. butter
1 tsp. vanilla extract

Mix together the cornstarch, sugar, and salt. Add a small amount of the milk and stir to make a paste. Then add remainder of the milk and cook over direct heat, stirring constantly, until thickened. Remove from the heat and add the butter and vanilla. Serve with plain cream or whipped cream. Serves 4.

Norwegian Pudding

1 recipe Vanilla Gelatin Pudding
   (see *Index*), omitting the crust

2 tbsps. raspberry syrup (drained
   from canned raspberries)
½ cup cream, whipped

Combine the raspberry syrup with the whipped cream and pour over the chilled pudding. Keep chilled until serving time.

Blackberry Tapioca Pudding

2 cups fresh blackberries
1 cup water

4 tbsp. quick-cooking tapioca
⅔ cup sugar

1 tbsp. lemon juice

Place the berries and water in a saucepan. Bring to a boil and simmer for 10 minutes. Strain. Discard seeds. Add enough water to the pulp and juice to make 2½ cups.

Mix the tapioca and sugar with the berry pulp and juice in a saucepan. Bring to a boil over medium heat, stirring constantly. Then add the lemon juice. Cool. Serve with plain cream or a dab of sour cream. Serves 4 to 5. *Variation:* Raspberries may be used instead of blackberries.

Apple Dessert

3-4 medium-size apples
1 cup water
½ cup sugar

1 tbsp. cornstarch
⅓ cup sugar
1 beaten egg

1 cup milk

Wash, peel, and slice the apples. Put the water, the ½ cup of sugar, and the apple slices in a saucepan and boil until the apples are soft. Remove the apple slices and place them in a casserole-type dish. Continue cooking the sugar and water mixture until it becomes syrupy; then pour over the apples. Make a boiled custard out of the remaining ingredients and pour it over the apples also. (If desired, ¼ teaspoon of lemon extract may be added to the custard.) Serves 4.

Rhubarb Pudding

1 cup rhubarb, cut in small pieces
¾ cup water
⅓ cup sugar

1 tbsp. cornstarch
1 egg, separated
1 tbsp. lemon juice

⅛ tsp. orange extract

Cook the rhubarb in ¾ cup water until done. Mix the sugar and cornstarch with the egg yolk. Slowly add the lemon juice. Combine this mixture with the cooked rhubarb and cook 3 or 4 minutes longer. Then fold in the stiffly beaten egg white and add the orange extract. Chill until serving time. Serves 4.

BAKED PUDDINGS

Plain Bread Pudding

2 cups dry bread crumbs or
  toast crumbs
4 cups milk
4 beaten eggs

⅔ cup sugar
1 tbsp. butter, melted
¼ tsp. salt
1 tsp. vanilla extract

¼ tsp. lemon or orange extract

Scald the milk and soak the bread crumbs in it for a few minutes. Add the beaten eggs, sugar, melted butter, salt, and flavorings. Pour into a greased 1½-quart baking dish, set in a pan of hot water, and bake in a moderate (350°) oven for 60 minutes. Serves 5 to 6.

Cocoa Bread Pudding

2 cups dry bread crumbs
4 cups milk, scalded
⅔ cup sugar
½ tsp. salt

1 tbsp. cocoa
3 beaten eggs
2 tbsps. melted butter
1 tsp. vanilla extract

Soak the crumbs in the scalded milk. Mix the sugar, salt, and cocoa with the beaten eggs. Combine with the soaked bread crumbs. Stir in the butter and vanilla and pour into a greased casserole. Set in a pan of hot water and bake at 350° for 1 hour. Serves 5 to 6.

Cocoa Meringue Pudding

1 tbsp. cocoa
⅔ cup sugar
½ tsp. salt

1 cup cooked rice
3 eggs, separated
2 cups heated milk

1 tsp. vanilla extract

Mix the cocoa, sugar, salt, and rice together. Add the beaten egg yolks, mix well, and stir in the heated milk. Cook in a double boiler until thickened, stirring constantly. Add the vanilla. Pour into a greased 1½-quart casserole.

Make a meringue by beating the egg whites until stiff, folding in 4 tablespoons sugar, and beating again. Spread on top of the pudding. Bake in a 350° oven for 12 to 15 minutes until the meringue is light brown. Serves 4 to 5.

Old-Fashioned Rice Pudding

⅔ cup quick-cooking rice

2¾ cups milk

⅓ cup sugar

½ tsp. salt

1 tsp. vanilla extract

1 tbsp. butter

Light brown sugar

Combine the rice, milk, sugar, salt, vanilla, and butter in a greased 1-quart baking dish. Bake in moderate (350°) oven for 1 hour, stirring once after 15 minutes and again after removing the pudding from the oven. Then sprinkle with light brown sugar and place under the broiler for a few minutes to brown. Serve warm or chilled. Serves 4.

Maple-Flavored Rice Pudding

1 cup quick-cooking rice

4½ cups milk

⅔ cup maple syrup

1 tsp. vanilla extract

½ tsp. salt

Put 4 cups of the milk in a saucepan and combine with the remaining ingredients. Bring to a boil. Then reduce heat and cook 30 minutes, stirring frequently. Remove from heat and stir in the remaining ½ cup milk. Pour into a greased 2-quart casserole and cool for 15 minutes. Sprinkle the top with brown sugar. Broil until the top is golden brown. Serves 4 to 5.

Blackberry Jelly Bread Pudding

1 cup dry bread crumbs

2 cups milk, scalded

2 eggs, separated

1 tbsp. butter, melted

⅔ cup confectioners' sugar

¼ tsp. lemon extract

½ tsp. vanilla extract

Blackberry jelly

Soak the bread crumbs in the scalded milk. Then run through a colander. Add beaten egg yolks, melted butter, sugar, and flavorings. Pour into a greased casserole and bake at 350° for 40 to 45 minutes. Remove from the oven and spread blackberry jelly over the top with light strokes.

Beat the egg whites until stiff, add 3 tablespoons confectioners' sugar and a few drops of lemon extract (if desired), and beat again. Spread the meringue on top of the jelly and return the pudding to the oven for 12 to 15 minutes until the meringue is light brown. Serves 5 to 6.

Butterscotch Bread Pudding

Make the same as Plain Bread Pudding, but use light brown sugar instead of white sugar and additional vanilla extract in place of the lemon or orange.

Lemon Bread Pudding

1 cup dry bread crumbs
1¾ cups milk, scalded
2 eggs, separated
½ cup sugar

¼ tsp. salt
1 tbsp. butter, melted
¼ tsp. orange extract
2 tbsps. lemon juice

Let the bread crumbs soak in the scalded milk for a few minutes. Beat the egg yolks and add them to the sugar, salt, and melted butter. Combine with the milk and bread-crumb mixture, the flavoring, and the lemon juice. Beat the egg whites until stiff and fold them in last. Bake in a greased casserole (set in a pan of hot water) at 350° for 40 to 45 minutes. Serves 4 to 5.

Rice Pudding Delight

¾ cup rice
2 cups milk
2 cups half-and-half cream
2 eggs, separated

¾ cup light brown sugar
¼ tsp. salt
1 tsp. vanilla extract
1 tbsp. butter

Cook the rice with the milk and cream in the top of a double boiler. Beat the egg yolks and then combine them with the sugar. Add the salt, vanilla, and butter and mix well. Stir in the hot rice. Cool before folding in the stiffly beaten egg whites. Pour into a greased casserole set in a pan of hot water. Bake in a 350° oven for 55 to 60 minutes. Serves 6.

Rice Pudding Supreme

1 cup cooked rice, strained
5 beaten eggs
1 cup cream, heated
1 cup milk, heated

½ tsp. salt
¾ cup sugar
1½ tsps. vanilla extract
1 tbsp. melted butter

Gradually combine the beaten eggs with the hot milk and cream, stirring well. Add the heated rice, salt, sugar, vanilla extract, and butter. Pour into a greased casserole set in pan of hot water. Bake in a 350° oven for 35 to 45 minutes. Serves 6.

Orange Meringue Rice Pudding

½ cup quick-cooking rice
2½ cups milk
½ tsp. salt

3 eggs, separated
2 tbsps. orange juice
⅔ cup sugar

Combine the rice, milk, and salt in a saucepan and cook over low heat until the rice is tender (about 20 minutes). In a large bowl, stir together the egg yolks, orange juice, and sugar. Gradually add the hot rice mixture, stirring thoroughly after each addition. Return to the pan and cook for 2 or 3 minutes over low heat. Pour into a greased casserole.

Beat the egg whites to make the meringue, adding 5 tablespoons of sugar and continuing to beat until stiff peaks are formed. Spread the meringue over the rice and bake for 8 to 10 minutes at 375°, or until lightly browned. Cool before serving. Serves 4 to 5.

Banana Wafer Pudding

Make alternate layers of vanilla wafers and sliced bananas in a greased casserole. Pour Vanilla Custard Sauce made with light brown sugar over the bananas (see *Sauces*).

Make a meringue by beating 2 egg whites until stiff and adding 2 tablespoons light brown sugar and ¼ teaspoon vanilla extract. Spread it over the pudding and bake in a 350° oven for 12 to 15 minutes. Serves 4 to 5.

Rhubarb Meringue Pudding

2 cups cooked rhubarb
⅔ cup sugar
2 tbsps. cornstarch

Dash of salt
1 cup milk
2 eggs, separated

1 tbsp. butter

Mix the sugar, cornstarch, and salt with a small amount of the milk to make a paste. Add the egg yolks and stir well. Add the remainder of the milk, and cook in a double boiler until thick. Add butter. Remove from heat. Put the cooked rhubarb in a greased baking dish and pour the hot custard sauce over the rhubarb.

Make a meringue by beating the 2 egg whites until stiff and adding 3 tablespoons sugar. Continue to beat until stiff peaks are formed. Spread on top of the rhubarb and custard, and bake for 6 to 8 minutes at 400° until the meringue is light brown. Serves 5.

Apple Crush

2 cups tart apple slices, peeled
⅓ cup light brown sugar
1 tbsp. lemon juice
¼ cup melted butter

1 cup cornflake crumbs or dry
  bread crumbs
¼ cup light brown sugar
⅓ cup orange-pineapple juice

Arrange 1 cup of the apple slices in the bottom of a greased 9-inch pie plate. Sprinkle with ⅓ cup light brown sugar and the lemon juice. Cover with the remaining apple slices. Combine the crumbs with the melted butter and the ¼ cup light brown sugar. Spread the crumb mixture over the apples. Pour the orange-pineapple juice mixture over the top. Bake in a 375° oven for 35 to 45 min. Serve plain or with Lemon Sauce (see *Sauces*). Serves 4 to 5.

Apple Pudding

1 apple, peeled and chopped fine
¾ cup sugar
2 tbsps. sifted flour

1 tsp. baking powder
2 beaten eggs
1 tsp. vanilla extract

¼ cup orange juice

Mix the dry ingredients together. Then stir in all the remaining ingredients and mix well. Pour into a greased casserole and bake in a 350° oven for 40 minutes. Serve with Orange Sauce (see *Sauces*). Serves 4 to 5.

Honey Apple Betty

2 cups tart apple slices, peeled
¼ cup light brown sugar
1 tbsp. orange juice
¼ cup strained honey

¾ cup vanilla water crumbs
2 tbsps. melted butter
¼ cup confectioners' sugar
⅓ cup pineapple-apricot juice

Arrange 1 cup of the apple slices in the bottom of a greased 9-inch pie plate. Sprinkle with the ¼ cup light brown sugar and the orange juice. Pour the honey on top. Add the remaining apple slices. Mix together the crumbs, butter, and confectioners' sugar and sprinkle the mixture over the apples. Then pour the fruit juice over. Bake in a 375° oven for 35 to 45 minutes. Serve plain or with sweetened whipped cream. Serves 4 to 5.

Baked Apple Surprise

5-6 tart apples, peeled and grated	¼ tsp. salt
½ cup sugar	3 eggs, separated
¼ cup butter	2 tbsps. lemon juice

Cream together the sugar and butter. Add the salt and egg yolks and beat until well blended. Add the lemon juice slowly and then the grated apples. Fold in the stiffly beaten egg whites last. Pour into a greased casserole and bake at 350° for 35 to 40 minutes. Serve with whipped cream or plain cream. Serves 5 to 6.

FROZEN DESSERTS

Vanilla Marlborough Dessert

15 marshmallows, diced	Dash of salt
¾ cup milk	1 tsp. vanilla extract
	1 cup cream, whipped

Dissolve the marshmallows in the milk in a double boiler. Cool. Add salt and flavoring, and chill. Fold the whipped cream into the marshmallow mixture and freeze in a refrigerator tray. Serves 5 to 6.

Banana Ice Cream

1 cup mashed bananas	¾ cup sugar
1 small can evaporated milk	1 tbsp. lemon juice

Chill the evaporated milk, a rotary beater, and a bowl in the refrigerator for an hour. Then whip the milk until it is thick. Add the sugar gradually. Add the mashed bananas mixed with the lemon juice. Put the mixture in a refrigerator tray and freeze. When it is frozen at the sides and on the bottom, raise the mixture with a spoon and allow the unfrozen part to run underneath. Resume freezing. Serves 5 to 6.

Floridian Ice Cream

1 banana	2 tbsps. lemon juice
¾ cup sugar	⅓ cup orange juice
1 cup milk	1 cup cream, whipped

Mash the banana, add the sugar, and mix to a smooth paste; add the milk. Stir in the fruit juices slowly and blend well. Pour into a refrigerator tray and freeze to the consistency of mush. Remove, fold in the whipped cream, and resume freezing. Serves 5 to 6.

Vanilla Ice Cream No. 1

1 tbsp. cornstarch	2 eggs, separated
½ cup sugar	4 tbsps. white corn syrup
2 cups milk	1 cup cream, whipped
	1 tsp. vanilla extract

Mix the cornstarch and sugar with enough milk to form a paste. Add beaten egg yolks, the remainder of the milk, and the corn syrup, mixing well. Cook over low heat until of custard consistency. Remove from stove, pour into a refrigerator tray, and freeze until mushy. Transfer to a chilled bowl. Beat the egg whites until stiff; beat the cream separately. Fold the egg whites and cream into the custard mixture. Add the vanilla. Return to the freezing tray and freeze. Serves 5 to 6.

Vanilla Ice Cream No. 2

2 eggs, separated	Juice of ½ lemon
½ cup sugar	1 cup evaporated milk
1 tsp. vanilla extract	1 cup milk

Beat the egg whites until stiff; add the sugar and continue beating. Then add the egg yolks and beat well. Stir in the flavoring and lemon juice, then both the evaporated and plain milk, and blend thoroughly. Pour into a chilled refrigerator tray and freeze. When partially frozen, transfer to a chilled bowl and whip until smooth. Return to the refrigerator tray and freeze until firm. Serves 5 to 6.

Lemon Custard Ice Cream

⅔ cup sugar	3 eggs, separated
Dash of salt	2 cups milk
2 tbsps. cornstarch	1 cup cream, whipped
	½ tsp. lemon extract

Mix the sugar, salt, and cornstarch. Add the egg yolks and stir well. Combine with the milk and cook in a double boiler until thick. Allow to cool. Beat the egg whites until stiff. Fold them into the cooked custard, along with the whipped cream and lemon extract. Pour into a refrigerator tray and freeze without stirring. Serves 5 to 6.

Caramel Ice Cream

⅔ cup light brown sugar
1 tbsp. butter
¾ cup water

4 beaten egg yolks
1 cup cream, whipped
1 tsp. vanilla extract

Cook the sugar, butter, and water until the sugar is melted and a light syrup is formed. Add this gradually to the egg yolks, beating thoroughly after each addition. Cook the mixture in a double boiler until thickened. Chill in the refrigerator. Then add the whipped cream and vanilla and pour into a refrigerator tray. Freeze without stirring. Serves 5 to 6.

Apricot Parfait

No. 303 can apricots, drained
   and strained
⅓ cup sugar

3 egg whites, beaten stiff
¼ tsp. almond flavoring
¾ cup cream, whipped

Add the sugar to the drained apricot juice and bring to a boil; then simmer 10 to 12 minutes to form a syrup. Add this to the stiffly beaten egg whites, beating constantly. Cool. Add the strained apricots and almond flavoring to the whipped cream and mix thoroughly. Then combine with the syrup mixture. Pour into a refrigerator tray and freeze without stirring. Serves 4 to 5.

Pineapple Parfait

1 cup pineapple juice
⅔ cup sugar

4 beaten egg yolks
1 cup cream, whipped quite stiff

Juice ½ lemon

Cook the pineapple juice and sugar together until syrupy. Add gradually to the beaten egg yolks, stirring rapidly after each addition. Cook the mixture in a double boiler until thickened. Cool. Add the lemon juice slowly. Combine the whipped cream with the cooled mixture, pour into a refrigerator tray, and freeze without stirring. Serves 5 to 6.

Orange Sherbet

1 pkg. orange gelatin
⅓ cup sugar
1 cup boiling water

1 cup evaporated milk
1 pt. milk
2 tbsps. orange juice

Dissolve the gelatin and sugar in the boiling water. Add both the evaporated and fresh milk, then the orange juice. Stir well and pour into a refrigerator tray. Freeze until firm. Then transfer to a chilled bowl and beat until smooth. Return to the tray and resume freezing. Serves 5 to 6.

California Sherbet

2 cups half-and-half cream   2 tbsps. lemon juice
¾ cup sugar   ½ cup fresh orange juice

Combine the cream and sugar and heat to the boiling point. Cool, pour into a refrigerator tray and freeze until mushy. Transfer to a large bowl, add the citrus juices, and beat until fluffy. Return to the tray and resume freezing. Serves 5 to 6.

Peach Mousse

1 cup canned soft peaches, mashed   2 tsps. lemon juice
¼ cup confectioners' sugar   ¼ tsp. almond extract
                    ¾ cup cream

Combine the sugar and peaches; then stir in the lemon juice and flavoring. Whip the cream and fold it into the peach mixture last. Pour into a refrigerator tray and freeze without stirring. Serves 4 to 5.

Applesauce Mousse

No. 303 can applesauce   1 tbsp. lemon juice
⅓ cup confectioners' sugar   ¼ tsp. lemon extract
2 tsps. strained honey   ¾ cup cream, whipped

Mix the applesauce with the honey and sugar. Stir in the lemon juice and flavoring. Then fold in the whipped cream. Pour into a refrigerator tray and freeze without stirring. Serves 4 to 5.

Prunella Mousse

1 cup cooked prunes, strained   2 tsps. honey
¼ cup confectioners' sugar   3 tbsps. orange juice
                    ¾ cup cream, whipped

Add the sugar and honey to the prunes. Stir in the orange juice. Fold in the whipped cream. Then pour into a refrigerator tray and freeze without stirring. Serves 4 to 5.

GELATIN DESSERTS

Gelatin recipes offer a wide variety of desserts for the person on an ulcer diet. They can be made in numerous colors and flavors and so help to relieve the monotony that sometimes makes a dieter rebel. Gelatin desserts also have the advantage of being quickly and easily made.

Various combinations of cooked fruits and fruit juices can be added to the gelatin base. When fruit juice is used, one cup of it should be substituted for one cup of the water used to dissolve the gelatin. For a different texture, try whipping the gelatin after it has started to thicken.

A colorful dessert can be made by preparing two different flavors of gelatin (orange and lime, for instance) in separate pans: Cut the congealed gelatin into 1-inch cubes, pile cubes of contrasting colors in alternate layers in glass dessert or sherbet dishes, and top with a dab of whipped cream.

Gelatin desserts are cooling and refreshing in warm weather, and since most of them are light and easy to digest, they make a fitting conclusion to a rich meal.

Eggnog Chiffon Pudding

1 envelope unflavored gelatin	1¾ cups milk
2 tbsps. sugar	1 tsp. rum extract
⅛ tsp. salt	¼ tsp. nutmeg (permanent ulcer diet)
3 eggs, separated	¼ cup sugar

Mix the gelatin, 2 tablespoons sugar, and the salt together in the top of a double boiler. Beat together the egg yolks and milk. Add to the gelatin mixture and cook over boiling water, stirring constantly, until the gelatin is thoroughly dissolved. Remove from the heat and add flavoring and nutmeg. Chill until the mixture mounds slightly when dropped from a spoon. Beat the egg whites until stiff; then beat in the ¼ cup sugar. Fold into the gelatin mixture, pile into sherbet glasses, and chill. Serves 6.

Pastel Pudding

1 pkg. raspberry gelatin	1¾ cups boiling water
1 pt. vanilla ice cream	

Dissolve the gelatin in boiling water. Add the ice cream by spoonfuls, stirring until melted. Chill until slightly thickened. Then pour into serving dishes and chill until firm. Serves 5.

Vanilla Gelatin Pudding

1 envelope unflavored gelatin
½ cup cold water
2 eggs, separated
½ cup sugar

½ cup scalded milk
1½ cups whipped cream
1 tsp. vanilla extract
8-inch Vanilla Wafer Crust
(made with light brown sugar)

Prepare a Vanilla Wafer Crust according to the directions under *Pastry*, substituting light brown sugar.

Soften the gelatin in cold water. Beat the egg yolks and mix with the sugar. Slowly add the milk. Cook in a double boiler until the mixture thickens. Remove from heat, stir in the gelatin, and blend well. Cool. Then fold in the whipped cream and vanilla extract. Fold in the stiffly beaten egg whites last. Pour into the prepared crust, sprinkle a few wafer crumbs over the top, and chill. Serves 5.

Variation: Fold in 2 mashed bananas and 1 tablespoon lemon juice.

Banana Whip

2 bananas, strained
1 pkg. orange gelatin

1 cup boiling water
1 cup cold water

1 tbsp. lemon juice

Dissolve the gelatin in the boiling water. Stir in cold water and lemon juice and chill until slightly thickened. Set the bowl of gelatin in a larger bowl of water containing ice cubes. Whip until fluffy and thick. Fold in the bananas, beating until well blended. Pour into a 1½-quart mold and chill until firm. Serves 5.

Cherry Surprise

1 pkg. cherry gelatin
1 cup boiling water
1 cup cold water
1 beaten egg

1½ bananas, mashed
1 tbsp. orange juice
1 tbsp. honey
¼ cup sugar

Few drops of lime juice

Dissolve the gelatin in boiling water. Add cold water and stir well. Pour into a mold and chill.

Mix all the remaining ingredients together until thoroughly blended. Chill. Serve as a sauce over the cherry gelatin. Serves 5.

Raspberry Refrigerator Pudding

1 pkg. raspberry gelatin
1 cup boiling water
¼ cup sugar

⅓ cup butter, melted
2 cups crushed vanilla wafers
1 small can evaporated milk

Chill the canned milk, a beater, and a bowl in the refrigerator for an hour. Meantime, mix together the melted butter and 1½ cups of wafer crumbs, and use to line a buttered casserole dish.

Add the boiling water to the gelatin and sugar, and stir until dissolved. Cool for a few minutes.

Whip the canned milk until stiff; then fold into the gelatin mixture and whip again. Pour into the crumb-lined dish and chill. Sprinkle the remaining ½ cup of crumbs over the top. Serves 6.

Cherry Gelatin Snow

1 pkg. cherry gelatin
1 cup hot water
1 cup pineapple juice

2 egg whites
¼ cup cream, whipped, sweetened, and flavored

Dissolve the gelatin in the hot water. Stir in the pineapple juice and chill until slightly thickened. Then add the egg whites, set the bowl in a pan containing water and ice cubes, and beat until the gelatin mixture is thick and fluffy. Pour into serving dishes and chill until firm. Serve with whipped cream. Serves 5.

Pineapple Snow

1 pkg. lime gelatin
1 cup boiling water

1 cup pineapple juice
⅛ tsp. salt

1 egg white

Dissolve the gelatin in boiling water. Stir in the pineapple juice and salt and chill until slightly thickened. Set the bowl in a larger pan containing ice and water. Add the egg white and whip until fluffy and thick. Spoon into sherbet glasses and chill until firm. Serve with Vanilla Custard Sauce (see Sauces). Serves 5 to 6.

Apricot Whip

1½ cups apricot nectar, heated
1 envelope unflavored gelatin

⅓ cup sugar
½ cup water

1 tbsp. lemon juice

Mix the gelatin and sugar together thoroughly. Add very hot nectar and stir until the gelatin is thoroughly dissolved. Add the water and lemon juice. Chill until slightly thicker than an unbeaten egg white. Then beat with a rotary beater until light and fluffy and double in volume. Turn into molds and chill until firm. Serves 4 to 5.

Cocoa—Marshmallow Dessert

1 tbsp. unflavored gelatin	1 cup milk
⅓ cup cold water	1 cup cream, whipped
¾ cup sugar	10 diced marshmallows
1 tbsp. cocoa	1 tsp. vanilla extract

Soften the gelatin in cold water. Mix the sugar and cocoa, add milk, and bring to a boil. Remove from the heat and stir in the gelatin. Chill until the mixture begins to set; then add the whipped cream, marshmallows, and vanilla. Chill again. Serves 5 to 6.

COOKED FRUIT DESSERTS

All fruits, including dried fruits, should be cooked and strained for the ulcer diet, with the exception of bananas. Skins and seeds should be discarded. As a person advances to the permanent ulcer diet, he may be able to eat soft canned peaches and apricots, unstrained—with his physician's permission, of course.

Strained cooked fruits can be served separately as a dessert, or combined with whipped cream, pudding mixtures, or gelatin dishes. A combination of several canned fruits or cooked fresh fruits, with a little honey or white corn syrup added, can be blended together into a delicious mixture in the blender. A tasty dish can also be prepared by blending three or four kinds of strained, cooked, dried fruits with a little sugar and lemon juice.

Rhubarb for Sauce

Wash rhubarb, cut out any dark or discolored areas from the skin, and cut into 1½-inch lengths. Put into a saucepan with ½ cup sugar to each 2 cups of rhubarb. Add a small amount of hot water and cook 20 to 25 minutes or until tender. A few drops of lemon juice may be added if desired. Serves 4 to 5.

Applesauce

Select a good grade of cooking apples. Wash well, remove the cores, but do not peel. Cut into quarters and cook with a small amount of water until soft. Strain, and add sugar to taste.

Stewed Dried Apricots

Soak the apricots overnight in cold water. Use the same water to cook, and cook with the pan covered. When the fruit is tender, strain. Add sugar, honey, or corn syrup to sweeten, and 1 tablespoon lemon juice if desired. Usually, ½ cup sugar is sufficient for 2 cups of fruit; cooking time is from 35 to 40 minutes. Serves 4 to 5.

Stewed Dried Peaches

Soak the peaches overnight in cold water. Use the same water to cook, and cook with the pan covered. When the fruit is tender, strain. Add about ½ cup sugar to 2 cups fruit. Usually, 40 to 45 minutes is sufficient cooking time. Serves 4 to 5.

Stewed Dried Prunes

Soak prunes for 1 hour in cold water. Use same water for cooking, adding a slice of orange for extra flavor. Cook the prunes slowly until tender; then strain. Sugar need not be added, since prunes contain natural sugar.

Apricot—Cherry Fruit Blend

¾ cup dried apricots (soaked overnight in a glass of warm water,
 then cooked and drained)
2 cups canned tart red cherries
 with juice

No. 2½ can soft peaches
No. 211 can crushed pineapple
¼ cup freshly squeezed orange juice
1 tbsp. honey
2 tbsps. white corn syrup

Cut the apricots and peaches into small pieces. Put all the fruits, with their juices and the other ingredients, into a large container. Transfer 2 cups of this fruit mixture at a time to the blender, and run at high speed. After all the fruit has been blended to a smooth consistency, stir together well and chill. Serve plain or with a dab of whipped cream and a cookie for dessert. Serves 8 to 10.

In all dessert recipes using whole apples, do not peel the fruit. Ulcer patients, however, should not eat the apple skin.

Plain Baked Apples

6 apples   6 tsps. butter
6 tbsps. white or light brown sugar

Wash the apples, remove the cores, and arrange apples in a greased baking dish. In the center of each put 1 teaspoon of butter and 1 tablespoon of sugar. Pour 1¼ cups of hot water in the baking dish and bake in a 350° oven for 1¼ hours, basting about every 20 minutes. Large apples may need to be cooked a little longer. Serves 6.

Variations: Fill the apple centers with either honey, confectioners' sugar, marshmallow, or red jelly, and serve with whipped cream on top.

Mapleine Baked Apples

6 tart apples   ½ cup maple syrup
1 tbsp. butter   ¾ cup hot water

Wash the apples and remove the cores. Arrange the apples in a greased casserole and put a bit of butter into each apple cavity. Pour the maple syrup on top. Put the hot water into the casserole; then bake in a 350° oven for 1¼ hours, or until the apples are tender. Serve with sweetened whipped cream to which a few drops of maple flavoring have been added. Serves 6.

Baked Apples with Cream Cheese

8-10 apples   2 3-oz. pkgs. cream cheese
¾ cup sugar   4 tsps. orange juice

Wash apples and remove cores. Arrange in a baking pan, standing the apples close together and pouring in enough boiling water to reach to ⅓ of their height. Add the sugar to the water. Bake for 40 minutes at 350°; then turn the apples over and bake 30 to 40 minutes, or until tender. Let cool. Stuff the apple centers with cream cheese thinned with orange juice. Serves 8 to 10.

Toasted Peaches

No. 2½ can soft peach halves   3 tbsps. lemon juice
¼ cup sugar   ¼ cup butter, melted
                    ⅔ cup cornflake crumbs

Drain the peaches. Combine the sugar and lemon juice, stirring until the sugar is dissolved. Dip the peach halves in the lemon juice mixture, then in melted butter. Roll in cornflake crumbs. Place peaches, cut side up, in a shallow baking pan. Bake in a moderate (350°) oven about 25 minutes. Serve warm with Vanilla or Lemon Sauce (see *Sauces*). Serves 4 to 6.

Sugar Plum Dessert

No. 2½ can purple plums   ⅛ tsp. cinnamon (permanent
1¾ cups lemon wafer crumbs   ulcer diet)
3 tbsps. butter   ¼ cup orange juice

Drain the syrup from the plums and set aside for use in the sauce. Remove plum pits, then strain the fruit.

Mix together the lemon wafer crumbs, 2 tablespoons of the butter, and the cinnamon. Arrange a layer of the crumbs in a baking dish, cover with strained fruit, and top with remaining crumbs. Pour orange juice over all and dot with 1 tablespoon of butter. Cover and bake in a 350° oven for 20 to 25 minutes. Serve with Fruit Sauce (below) and sprinkle jumbo sugar crystals over the top of the sauce. Serves 5 to 6.

Fruit Sauce

¼ cup butter   1 tbsp. lemon juice
1 cup sifted confectioners' sugar   ¼ cup plum syrup

Whip the butter with the confectioners' sugar until smooth and fluffy. Add the lemon juice. Whip the syrup into the butter mixture until the sauce has a smooth consistency.

FRUIT WHIPS

Fruit whips are light, fluffy mixtures having, usually, stiffly beaten egg whites as a base, with fruits and a sweetener added. These desserts are sometimes baked, sometimes not. Whipped cream replaces the egg whites in some of the whips.

Fruit whips are especially appropriate desserts to serve in the summertime or after a heavy meal.

Prune Whip

1 cup cooked prunes, strained
¼ cup confectioners' sugar

2 tsps. orange juice
2 stiffly beaten egg whites

Fold prunes, sugar, and orange juice into the egg whites and blend well. Chill. Serves 4 to 5.

Peach Whip

1 cup soft canned peaches, strained
1 tbsp. lemon juice

¼ cup confectioners' sugar
½ cup cream, whipped

2 stiffly beaten egg whites

Add the lemon juice to the peaches. Fold in the confectioners' sugar and whipped cream. Fold in the egg whites last. Blend well, then chill. Serves 4 to 5.

Baked Vanilla Prune Whip

1 cup cooked prunes, strained
¼ cup sugar

¼ tsp. vanilla extract
3 stiffly beaten egg whites

Fold prunes, sugar, and vanilla extract into the egg whites. Blend well. Pour into a greased casserole and bake in a 350° oven for 20 to 25 minutes. Serves 5 to 6. (Prune whips may be served with dab of whipped cream or Lemon Sauce—see *Sauces*).

Apple Froth

4 cooking apples
⅔ cup boiling water

⅓ cup confectioners' sugar
Dash of salt

3 beaten egg whites

Wash, peel, and core the apples; then cut them into small pieces. Cook in the boiling water with a few drops of orange juice until the apples are tender. Strain. Fold the sugar, salt, and apple mixture into the egg whites. Serve chilled with Orange Sauce (see *Sauces*). Serves 5 to 6.

Dried Apricot Whip

1-lb. pkg. dried apricots	2 tsps. honey
2 tsps. orange juice	¾ cup granulated sugar

3 beaten egg whites

Cook the apricots until tender; then drain and strain. Add the orange juice, honey, and sugar to the apricot pulp and cook for a few minutes over low heat until the sugar is dissolved. Then cool. Fold into the stiffly beaten egg whites. Serve with whipped cream or Lemon Sauce (see *Sauces*). Serves 6.

MISCELLANEOUS DESSERTS

Apricot Rice Pudding

1 cup strained canned apricots	⅓ cup confectioners' sugar
2 cups cooked rice	¼ tsp. lemon extract

1 cup cream, whipped

Stir the apricots into the rice. Add sugar and flavoring and blend well. Fold in the whipped cream. Serve chilled. Serves 6.

Banana–Apricot Dessert

3-4 bananas, mashed	½ cup light brown sugar
1 pkg. dried apricots, cooked and strained	1 tbsp. orange juice
	½ cup cream, whipped

Add the brown sugar to the strained apricots. Fold in the mashed bananas, orange juice, and whipped cream. Serve chilled. Serves 5 to 6.

Frosted Vanilla Wafers

1 pkg. vanilla wafers	½ tsp. vanilla extract
2 tbsps. sugar	1 cup cream, whipped

Add sugar and vanilla extract to the whipped cream. Allow 6 cookies for each serving, piling them on top of one another and spreading a generous amount of whipped cream between and on top. Serves 6. (Each cookie stack may be topped with a maraschino cherry if the patient is on the permanent ulcer diet.)

Fruit Compote

1 cup strained cooked prunes
1 cup strained canned apricots
1 cup strained canned Elberta
   peaches

1 tbsp. lemon juice
1 tbsp. orange juice
1 tbsp. honey

Mix all ingredients together and chill. Serves 4.

Nassau Banana Dessert

5 bananas
2 tbsps. pineapple juice
2 tbsps. orange juice

2 tbsps. lemon juice
¼ cup light brown sugar
1 tbsp. butter

Peel the bananas, cut in half lengthwise, and arrange in a greased casserole. Mix the fruit juices with brown sugar and pour over the bananas. Dot with butter. Bake in a 400° oven about 12 minutes or until done. Serve with hot Rum Sauce (follow recipe for Vanilla Custard Sauce, substituting ½ teaspoon rum extract for the vanilla).

Jellied Apples

No. 303 can sliced apples
½ cup sugar

Dash of salt
1 tbsp. quick-cooking tapioca
   ½ cup water

Mix the sugar, salt, and tapioca together. Add the apples and water and cook over low heat about 15 minutes, until the apples are tender and the mixture has thickened. Strain and chill. Serves 5 to 6.

Marshmallow Dandy Dessert

½ lb. marshmallows
½ cup milk, heated

1 cup cream, whipped
1 tsp. vanilla extract
   1½ cups vanilla wafer crumbs

Put the marshmallows and hot milk in a double boiler and cook until the marshmallows are melted, stirring constantly. Allow to cool. Then combine with the whipped cream and add the flavoring.

Spread 1 cup wafer crumbs in the bottom of a 1-quart mold. Pour in the marshmallow mixture, sprinkle the remaining ½ cup crumbs on top, and chill for several hours. Serves 5 to 6.

Angel Peach Dessert

2 cups peach nectar
¼ cup quick-cooking tapioca
½ cup sugar

¼ cup orange juice
6 diced marshmallows
Angel food or sponge cake squares

Mix tapioca and sugar; then add the peach nectar and orange juice. Cook over low heat until the mixture starts to thicken, about 5 minutes. Remove from the heat and stir in the marshmallows. Put squares of sponge or angel food cake in a greased casserole. Pour the tapioca mixture over the cake, cover with additional squares of cake, and set in the refrigerator for 8 to 10 hours before serving. Serve chilled, with whipped cream on top. Serves 6 to 8.

CAKES

Cake is often forbidden on the ulcer diet in the earlier stages. Later, when it is permitted, usually the more simple types of cakes, such as angel food, sponge cake, and chiffon cake, are allowed. Cake, as well as other sweets, should be served in moderate amounts on the bland diet.

Good organization insures better baking. Have all the ingredients necessary for a cake, as well as the required equipment, ready before starting. Eggs and other ingredients should be at room temperature. Use large eggs, unless the recipe calls for small ones. Successful cake-baking depends as much on careful and correct measurements as on the proper mixing of ingredients. Also important is the correct oven heat.

Most angel food and sponge cakes are baked in tube pans, though sponge cakes can be baked in layers. Chocolate ice-cream roll and various jelly rolls are baked in a shallow pan 15½" x 10½" x 1".

ANGEL FOOD AND SPONGE CAKES

Substitute Angel Food Cake

1⅓ cups cake flour
1½ tsps. baking powder
Dash of salt
1 cup sugar

½ cup milk, heated
½ tsp. vanilla extract
¼ tsp. almond flavoring
4 egg whites

Sift the dry ingredients three times after measuring. Add heated milk, a little at a time, and the flavorings. Beat the egg whites until stiff and fold them into batter last. Bake in an ungreased tube pan in a 350° oven for 30 to 40 minutes. Serves 6.

Angel Food Cake

1 cup sifted cake flour	¼ tsp. salt
1½ cups sugar	1¼ tsps. cream of tartar
1½ cups egg whites (about 12)	1 tsp. vanilla extract
	½ tsp. orange or lemon extract

Sift the flour with ½ cup sugar 6 times, using triple-screen sifter. Beat the egg whites, cream of tartar, salt, and extracts until the mixture stands in soft peaks that are still glossy and moist. Add the remaining 1 cup of sugar, 3 tablespoons at a time, beating after each addition until well blended. Using a large spoon, fold in the flour in 4 steps, blending well.

Pour the batter into a lightly floured, ungreased 10-inch tube pan. Bake in a 375° oven for 35 to 40 minutes. Cool the cake in the pan, upside down on a cake rack. After 1 hour, the cake may be removed by running a knife around the sides and the spout. Serves 10 to 12.

Variations: Follow the directions for plain angel food cake, but use ¾ cup of flour and ¼ cup of cocoa, sifting the cocoa the same number of times as the flour.

For other variations in flavoring, try 1 teaspoon maple extract, or ½ teaspoon of almond and ½ teaspoon peppermint extracts, or 1 teaspoon almond extract and 2 teaspoons of maraschino cherry juice.

Small Sponge Cake Squares (Warm Water)

3 eggs, separated	¼ cup warm water
1 cup sugar	1 cup cake flour
1 tsp. almond extract	1 tsp. baking powder
	¼ tsp. salt

Beat the egg yolks and add half of the sugar. Stir in the flavoring and warm water. Beat the egg whites until stiff, and then beat in the remainder of the sugar until well blended. Add sifted dry ingredients to the egg yolk mixture. Fold this batter into the egg white mixture. Pour into an ungreased loaf pan and bake in a 325° oven about 1 hour. Cut into squares when cool. Serves 10.

Angel Food Individual Loaves

With a serrated knife, cut angel food cake into 3 layers; then cut these into small, rectangular-shaped loaves or—using cookie cutters—into fancy shapes. Frost with plain boiled icing or sweetened, flavored whipped cream. Serves several, depending on the number of cakes cut. (For special occasions, the icing may be tinted a different color for each cake.)

Sunshine Sponge Cake

8 egg yolks	1⅓ cups cake flour, sifted
1⅓ cups sugar, sifted	2 tsps. baking powder
⅔ cup cold water	¼ tsp. salt

½ tsp. orange or lemon extract

Beat the egg yolks until thick and lemon-colored. Add the sugar gradually, beating well after each addition. Add the cold water and flavoring and continue beating. Add flour, baking powder, and salt, which have been sifted 3 times after measuring. Beat again until smooth.

Pour into a greased and floured tube pan and bake in slow (325°) oven for 15 minutes; then increase the heat to 350° and bake 1 hour. Serves 10.

Sponge Cake Delight

1¼ cups cake flour, sifted	1 tsp. cream of tartar
¼ tsp. baking powder	1½ cups sugar
¼ tsp. salt	⅓ cup cold water
5 large eggs, separated	1 tsp. vanilla extract

¼ tsp. orange extract

Sift the flour, baking powder, and salt 3 times after measuring. Beat the egg whites until foamy, then add cream of tartar. Continue beating until the whites stand in peaks. Gradually add half of the sugar to the egg whites, beating well.

Beat the yolks until thick and lemon-colored. Add water, the remaining sugar, and the flavorings. Beat well again. Fold the dry ingredients into egg yolk mixture. Then carefully fold in the egg whites until well blended.

Pour into a large ungreased tube pan and bake in a slow (325°) oven for 75 minutes. Cool upside down on a rack for 50 to 60 minutes. Serves 8 to 10.

Variations: For special occasions, split the cake into two layers, spread apricot preserves (permanent ulcer diet) between the layers, and sprinkle confectioners' sugar over the top. Or whipped cream may be spread over the top and sides of the cake.

Jelly Roll

3 eggs, separated	1 tsp. baking powder
1 cup confectioners' sugar	Dash of salt
1 tbsp. milk or cream	¼ tsp. lemon extract
1 cup flour	½ tsp. vanilla extract

Beat the egg yolks for 2 minutes with an electric mixer. Add half of the sugar and continue to beat until smooth. Beat the egg whites until stiff; slowly add the remaining sugar and beat again until shiny and smooth. Add the sifted dry ingredients and the milk or cream to the egg yolks. Fold this batter, with flavorings, into the egg white mixture.

Pour into a shallow jelly-roll pan (15½" x 10½" x 1") lined with greased, waxed paper. Bake in a 375° oven for 12 to 14 minutes. When the cake is done, run a knife around the sides of the pan to loosen, and turn out on a towel sprinkled with confectioners' sugar. Remove the waxed paper and trim the crusts. Roll the cake in the towel to cool. Unroll, remove towel, and spread cake with raspberry jelly. Roll again. Serves 8 to 10.

Blackberry Jelly Roll

3 eggs, separated	1 tsp. baking powder
¾ cup granulated sugar	¼ tsp. salt
1 tbsp. melted butter	1 tbsp. cream
1 cup flour	1 tsp. vanilla extract

Mix the ingredients as in the preceding jelly roll recipe, adding the melted butter to the egg yolks at the same time the sugar is added. Bake in a 375° oven for 12 to 14 minutes. Run a knife around the sides to loosen the cake, and turn it out on a towel sprinkled with confectioners' sugar. Remove the waxed paper and trim off the crusts. Roll in a towel to cool. Unroll, remove towel, and spread with blackberry jelly. Roll again. Serves 8 to 10.

Cocoa Whipped Cream Log

5 eggs, separated
1 cup sugar
Dash of salt

1 tsp. baking powder
3 tbsps. flour
2 tbsps. cocoa

1 tsp. vanilla extract

Beat the egg yolks for 2 minutes with an electric mixer. Add ½ cup of sugar and continue to beat until smooth. Beat the egg whites until stiff; slowly add ½ cup sugar and beat again until shiny and smooth. Add the sifted dry ingredients and flavoring to the egg yolks. Fold this batter into the egg whites.

Pour into a shallow jelly-roll pan (15½" x 10½" x 1") lined with greased, waxed paper. Bake in a 325° oven for 25 to 30 minutes. Then run a knife around sides to loosen the cake, and while it is still warm turn out on a towel sprinkled with confectioners' sugar. Remove the waxed paper and trim off the crusts. Roll the cake in the towel and cool. Unroll, remove towel, and spread cake with sweetened, flavored whipped cream. Roll again. Serves 8 to 10.

Apricot Skillet Cake

Topping

1 cup canned soft apricots, drained (permanent ulcer diet)
3 tbsps. butter
⅔ cup light brown sugar

Dash of salt
1 small bottle maraschino cherries, drained

Melt the butter in a 9-inch skillet. Spread the brown sugar smoothly over the bottom of the skillet, and add a dash of salt. Place apricots, hollow side up, on the sugar. Put a maraschino cherry in each apricot hollow (cherries are for decoration only).

Sponge Batter

3 eggs, separated
1 scant cup sugar
¼ cup apricot syrup
¼ tsp. almond extract

1 tsp. vanilla extract
1 cup sifted cake flour
1 tsp. baking powder
¼ tsp. salt

Beat the egg yolks until thick and lemon-colored. Add the sugar gradually and beat well; then add the fruit syrup and flavorings. Fold in the sifted dry ingredients. Beat the egg whites until stiff and fold them in last. Pour the batter into the skillet on top of the fruit. Bake in a 375° oven for 45 minutes. Remove from the oven and let stand for 5 to 7 minutes. Then turn upside down. Serve plain or with dabs of whipped cream. Serves 8 to 10.

Whipped Cream Cake

2 cups cake flour, sifted	1¼ cups sugar, sifted
2 tsps. baking powder	½ cup milk
¼ tsp. salt	1½ tsps. vanilla extract
3 egg whites	1 cup cream, whipped

Sift flour, baking powder, and salt 4 times. Beat the egg whites until they form peaks but still cling to the sides of the bowl. Add the sugar gradually in 3 or 4 steps, and beat until well blended with the whites. Then fold in the dry ingredients alternately with the milk and vanilla. Fold in the whipped cream last. Bake in greased, floured pans in a 350° oven for 35 to 45 minutes, or until done. Serves 8 to 10.

CHIFFON CAKES

Orange Chiffon Cake

2¼ cups cake flour, sifted	5 unbeaten egg yolks
2 tsps. baking powder	Juice of 2 oranges, plus water
1½ cups sugar	to make ¾ cup
¼ tsp. salt	½ tsp. lemon extract
½ cup salad oil	1 cup egg whites (8-10)
½ tsp. cream of tartar	

Measure the dry ingredients into a bowl and sift 3 times. Make a well in the middle of the flour mixture and pour in the salad oil, egg yolks, orange juice, and flavoring. Beat with a large spoon until very smooth.

Measure the egg whites and cream of tartar into a large bowl. Beat with a wire whisk or an electric beater until they form very stiff peaks. They should be very stiff (stiffer than a pie meringue). Gradually fold the egg yolk mixture into the whipped egg whites. Blend well.

Pour the batter into an ungreased 10-inch tube pan. Bake in a preheated oven at 325° for 55 minutes; then in a moderate (350°) oven for 10 to 15 minutes. Serves 10.

Tropical Chiffon Cake

2¼ cups sifted cake flour
2 tsps. baking powder
1½ cups sugar
¼ tsp. salt
½ cup salad oil

5 unbeaten egg yolks
¼ cup orange juice
½ cup pineapple juice (remove 2 tbsps. and add 2 tbsps. lemon juice)
1 cup egg whites (8-10)

½ tsp. cream of tartar

Follow the mixing directions given for Orange Chiffon Cake (preceding). Serves 10.

CHEESE CAKES

Cheese cakes are rich, and the patient on an ulcer diet should eat only a small serving and should avoid eating other rich foods at the same meal.

Gelatin Cottage Cheese Cake

Step 1:

Mix the following ingredients together and cook in a double boiler until the gelatin is dissolved and the mixture slightly thickened:

2 envelopes unflavored gelatin
3 beaten egg yolks

6 tbsps. sugar
1½ cups milk

¼ tsp. salt

Remove from heat and stir in ½ teaspoon lemon extract. Chill until the mixture starts to thicken.

Step 2:

3 cups creamed cottage cheese
1 tbsp. lemon juice
1 tsp. vanilla extract

3 egg whites, beaten stiff
6 tbsps. sugar
⅓ cup vanilla wafer crumbs

While the gelatin is chilling, beat the creamed cottage cheese at high speed with an electric mixer for 3 minutes. Stir in the lemon juice and vanilla. Fold in the cooled gelatin mixture.

Beat the egg whites until stiff. Add the sugar gradually and continue to beat until very stiff. Fold into the gelatin mixture, then turn into an 8-inch spring-form pan. Sprinkle the top with vanilla wafer crumbs. Chill until firm. Serves 8 to 10.

Lemon Cheese Cake

2 eggs	1 pkg. cream cheese (8 ozs.)
⅓ cup sugar	1 pkg. cream cheese (3 ozs.)
½ tsp. lemon extract	9-inch Vanilla Wafer Crust (unbaked)
	(see *Pastry and Pies*)

Put the eggs, sugar, and flavoring in a bowl and beat well. Add the cream cheese, a small amount at a time, beating well after each addition. Pour into the prepared crust, spreading smoothly over the bottom. Cover the pan and bake in a 350° oven for 30 minutes.

Topping

Mix together 1 cup dairy sour cream, 3 tablespoons sugar, and ½ teaspoon lemon extract, and stir until well blended. Spread over the baked cheese mixture, cover, and bake at 400° for 5 minutes. Cool. Store in the refrigerator until serving time. Serves 10.

Orange Cheese Cake

1 pkg. orange gelatin	¾ cup sugar
1 cup boiling water	½ tsp. lemon extract
3 tbsps. orange juice	1 tall can evaporated milk
1 pkg. cream cheese (8 ozs.)	1⅓ cups vanilla wafer crumbs
¼ cup butter, melted	

Chill the canned milk, a rotary beater, and a bowl for at least an hour. Let the cream cheese soften.

Dissolve the gelatin in boiling water. Add the orange juice; then cool. Beat the softened cream cheese together with the sugar and flavoring. Combine with the gelatin mixture. Whip the canned milk and fold it in last.

Reserve ½ cup of the wafer crumbs for the top of the cake. Mix the remainder with the melted butter and use to line a 9-inch cake pan. Pour in the gelatin filling, sprinkle the reserved crumbs over the top, and chill in the refrigerator until set. Serves 8 to 10.

CAKE FROSTINGS, FILLINGS, AND TOPPINGS

Whipped cream makes an attractive as well as delicious frosting for the angel food and sponge cakes on this diet. Use it either plain or sweetened with a small amount of sugar; add any favorite flavoring. For festive occasions, a few drops of food coloring may also be added.

On the ulcer diet, cream and fruit custards are desirable fillings to spread between the layers of a sponge cake. Jelly may also be used as a filling.

Often these cakes simply have confectioners' sugar lightly sprinkled over the top, but recipes are given here for other toppings made with fruit, eggs, sugar, corn syrup, or whipped cream.

Plain Boiled Icing

½ cup sugar
3 tbsps. water

⅛ tsp. cream of tartar
1 egg white, unbeaten

¼ tsp. lemon extract

Combine all the ingredients except the flavoring, and cook in a double boiler. Beat constantly until the mixture is thick and stands up in peaks. Remove from the heat, add flavoring, and beat well. Boiled Icing is delicious on both angel food and sponge cake.

Sea-Foam Icing

½ cup light brown sugar
3 tbsps. water

⅛ tsp. cream of tartar
1 egg white, unbeaten

½ tsp. vanilla extract

Combine the sugar, water, cream of tartar, and egg white and cook in a double boiler, beating constantly with a rotary beater until the mixture is thick and stands in peaks. Remove from the stove, add flavoring, and beat well.

Orange Boiled Icing

2 tbsps. orange juice
½ cup sugar
1 tbsp. water

⅛ tsp. cream of tartar
1 egg white, unbeaten
⅛ tsp. orange or lemon extract

Combine all the ingredients with the exception of the flavoring and cook in a double boiler, beating constantly until thick and the mixture stands in peaks. Remove from the stove, add flavoring, and beat well.

Pineapple 7-Minute Icing

1 egg white, unbeaten
2 tbsps. syrup from canned
   pineapple

¾ cup sugar
⅛ tsp. salt
⅛ tsp. cream of tartar

¼ tsp. lemon extract

Cook all the ingredients except the flavoring in a double boiler, beating until the mixture thickens and stands in peaks. Remove from the heat, add the flavoring, and beat well. Spread on the cake in swirls.

Peppermint Striped Frosting

1 cup sugar
3 tbsps. cold water
2 egg whites

½ tsp. white corn syrup
¼ tsp. cream of tartar
¼ tsp. orange extract

¼ cup crushed peppermint stick candy

Mix the sugar, water, egg whites, corn syrup, and cream of tartar in the top of a double boiler and cook for 5 minutes, beating constantly with a rotary or electric beater until the mixture stands in peaks. Remove from the heat and add the flavoring and peppermint candy. Stir well. Makes enough for one cake.

Apple Whip Filling

3 large apples
⅔ cup sugar

1 tbsp. cornstarch
Juice of 1 lemon

1 egg yolk

Wash, peel, and grate the apples. (Or put quarters of peeled apple into a blender for a few minutes.) Set aside. Mix together the sugar, corn-starch, and lemon juice; add the egg yolk and mix well. Stir in the grated apples last. Cook over low heat for 10 to 15 minutes until the mixture thickens, stirring constantly. Cool before spreading on the cake. Recipe makes enough filling for 2 layers.

Quick Caramel Icing

½ cup light brown sugar
2 tbsps. butter

2 tbsps. half-and-half cream
½ cup confectioners' sugar

½ tsp. vanilla extract

Combine the brown sugar and butter and cook over low heat until the mixture comes to a full boil. Add the cream and continue cooking 3 or 4 minutes. Remove from heat and add confectioners' sugar and flavoring. Makes enough for 1 cake.

Orange Fluff Icing

2 tbsps. butter
1¼ cups sifted confectioners' sugar
1 egg white

½ tsp. orange extract
Dash of cinnamon (permanent
   ulcer diet)

Cream the butter with ¾ cup of the confectioners' sugar. Beat the egg white until stiff; then fold in ½ cup confectioners' sugar, the orange extract, and a dash of cinnamon. Combine the two mixtures and blend thoroughly. Makes enough for 1 cake.

Orange Filling

⅓ cup sugar
2 tbsps. cornstarch
½ cup water

⅔ cup orange juice
2 tbsps. lemon juice
2 tbsps. butter

Mix together the sugar and cornstarch. Add the water gradually to form a paste. Then stir in the fruit juices and butter. Cook over low heat, stirring constantly, until the mixture has thickened. Cool before using. Recipe makes enough filling for 2 layers.

Whipped Cream Topping

1 cup cream, whipped

1 tbsp. sugar

¼ tsp. vanilla extract

Beat the cream until stiff. Add the sugar and vanilla. The topping may be spread on the cake a few hours ahead of serving time and the cake stored in the refrigerator. A few drops of food coloring may be added. Makes enough for 1 angel food cake.

Orange Topping

2 beaten egg yolks   Juice of 1 orange
½ cup sugar   1 cup cream, whipped
                    ¼ tsp. lemon extract

Mix the egg yolks with the sugar. Add the orange juice slowly and cook in a double boiler until thickened, stirring constantly. Cool. Then add the whipped cream and flavoring. Spread on top of an angel food cake or chiffon cake. Keep in the refrigerator until serving time.

Banana Topping

2 egg whites   1 mashed banana
¼ cup confectioners' sugar   ½ tsp. vanilla extract
                    ½ cup cream, whipped

Beat the egg whites until stiff. Fold in the confectioners' sugar, banana, and vanilla flavoring, then the whipped cream. (This topping should be made only a short time before using and should be stored in the refrigerator.) Use on sponge, chiffon or angel food cake.

Variation: Add a mixture of strained canned fruits, with honey and lemon or orange juice.

Lemon Filling

⅔ cup sugar   1 tbsp. lemon juice
1 tbsp. cornstarch   1 egg yolk
Juice 1 orange   1 cup boiling water
                    2 tsps. butter

Mix the sugar and cornstarch with a small amount of fruit juice and stir into a smooth paste. Add the egg yolk and mix well. Add the remainder of the fruit juices and 1 cup boiling water. Cook in a double boiler until thick. Add butter and cool. Makes enough filling for 2 layers of sponge cake.

Pink Fluff Topping

Combine, in a double boiler, 1 unbeaten egg white and ⅓ cup of tart jelly (grape or raspberry) with ⅛ teaspoon salt. Beat constantly with a rotary beater while cooking. When the topping is stiff, remove from heat and cool. Use for sponge or chiffon cake.

Peach Filling

1 tbsp. cornstarch	1 cup peach nectar
Dash of salt	2 tsps. butter
⅓ cup sugar	¼ tsp. almond extract
1 egg yolk	2 tsps. maraschino cherry juice

Mix the cornstarch, salt, and sugar together. Add the egg yolk and stir until well blended. Gradually add the nectar and cook in a double boiler until thick. Remove from heat and add the butter, flavoring, and maraschino cherry juice. Makes enough filling for 2 layers of sponge cake.

Cream Filling

⅔ cup sugar	2 beaten eggs
¼ cup cornstarch	2 cups milk, scalded
Dash of salt	1 tsp. vanilla extract

Mix together the dry ingredients; then add the beaten eggs. Add the scalded milk gradually, stirring well after each addition. Cook in a double boiler until thickened (about 15 minutes), stirring constantly. Cool before adding the vanilla. If the filling is lumpy, beat well with a rotary beater. Makes enough filling for 2 sponge layers.

Variation: For the permanent ulcer diet, 1 teaspoon decaffeinated instant coffee can be added with the dry ingredients to make Coffee Cream Filling.

COOKIES

The ulcer diet usually permits only plain cookies, such as vanilla wafers, and cookies without roughage or heavy spices. But even with these limitations, a considerable variety can be achieved by using different flavorings and making different types of cookies—drop, refrigerator, rolled, pressed, and formed or shaped. Decorating cookies with colored sugar or dabs of tinted icing adds to their eye appeal.

Successful cookie-making calls for good ingredients, the proper equipment, and some advance organization. You will save time and labor if you assemble all the ingredients in order before beginning. Cookie sheets should be made of heavy aluminum. It is useful to own two of them, so that while one batch of cookies is cooling, the next can be arranged on the second cookie sheet ready for baking. When cookie sheets are to be greased, an unsalted shortening is usually preferable. Preheat the oven before beginning to mix the ingredients. While the cookies are baking, do not open the oven door unnecessarily.

Cookies served with fruit or custard are an acceptable dessert for either lunch or dinner. They are also useful and popular as lunch-box desserts, between-meal snacks, and quick refreshments for unexpected callers.

DROP COOKIES

Drop cookies are simple to make. The batter or dough should be dropped from a teaspoon onto the cookie sheet without crowding. Allow 2 inches between cookies and keep the dough at least an inch from the edge of the cookie sheet. These cookies can be made small and dainty for teas and parties, or large enough to satisfy the most robust appetite.

Honey Chews

¼ cup butter	1½ cups flour
¼ cup sugar	½ tsp. baking soda
1 beaten egg	3 tbsps. lemon juice
½ cup honey	⅛ tsp. lemon extract

Cream together the butter and sugar. Add the egg and honey and stir well. Stir in the sifted dry ingredients alternately with the lemon juice and flavoring. Drop the dough by spoonfuls on a greased cookie sheet and bake in a 350° oven for 10 to 12 minutes. Makes 4 dozen cookies.

Snow Cookies with Cherry Tops

¾ cup butter	½ tsp. almond extract
¾ cup confectioners' sugar	2 cups sifted flour
2 egg yolks	Bits of maraschino cherry for decoration

Cream together the butter and sugar. Add the egg yolks and flavoring and mix well. Add the flour. Drop by spoonfuls on an ungreased cookie sheet. Decorate with bits of maraschino cherry. Bake in a 350° oven for 15 to 18 minutes. Makes about 3 dozen cookies.

Vanilla Wafers

1 cup sugar
¼ cup butter or margarine
2 beaten eggs
1½ tsps. vanilla extract

1½ cups sifted flour
¼ tsp. salt
1½ tsps. baking powder
¼ cup half-and-half cream

Cream the sugar and butter. Add the eggs and flavoring. Mix in the dry ingredients alternately with the cream, and blend well. Drop by spoonfuls on a greased cookie sheet. Bake in a 350° oven for 7 or 8 minutes or until done. Makes about 2½ dozen cookies.

Buttermilk Crumb Cookies

1 cup sugar
½ cup vegetable shortening
1 beaten egg
¼ tsp. lemon extract
1 tsp. vanilla extract

1 tsp. baking soda mixed with
    ½ cup buttermilk
½ tsp. salt
½ tsp. baking powder
1½ cups sifted flour

1½ cups dry bread crumbs

Cream together the sugar and shortening. Add the egg and flavorings and mix well. Sift all dry ingredients except crumbs, and add alternately with the buttermilk mixture. Stir in the crumbs last. Drop from a teaspoon on a greased cookie sheet and bake in a 350° oven about 10 minutes. Makes about 5 dozen cookies.

Danish Cone Cookies

3 egg whites
½ cup sugar
⅓ cup cake flour
⅓ cup butter, melted and cooled

Dash of salt
1½ tsps. vanilla extract
½ cup cream, whipped
2 tsps. sugar

Beat the egg whites until stiff; add sugar, a little at a time, mixing well. Gradually fold in the sifted cake flour. Then fold in the butter, salt, and 1 teaspoon of the vanilla. Drop spoonfuls of the batter on a buttered and floured cookie sheet, about 2 inches apart. Bake at 375° about 10 minutes, until lightly browned.

Remove from the oven and quickly shape the cookies into hollow cones by overlapping the edges. If the cookies harden too quickly, return them to the oven for a minute or two. When the cones are cool, fill with whipped cream to which ½ teaspoon vanilla and 2 teaspoons sugar have been added. Makes about 2 dozen.

Chocolate–Vanilla Chews

¼ cup butter

¾ cup sugar

1 beaten egg

½-oz. square unsweetened
    chocolate, melted

1 tsp. vanilla extract

½ cup undiluted evaporated milk

1½ cups sifted flour

¼ tsp. salt

¼ tsp. baking soda

¼ tsp. baking powder

Cream the shortening and sugar; add the egg and beat well. Stir in the melted chocolate, then the flavoring and evaporated milk, and blend thoroughly. Add the sifted dry ingredients. Drop teaspoonfuls of the dough on a greased baking sheet. Bake in a 425° oven about 8 minutes. (Chocolate is often restricted on the ulcer diet; therefore small amounts are used in these recipes.) Makes about 3 dozen cookies.

Almond Mint Cookies

1 cup vegetable shortening

1 cup light brown sugar,
    firmly packed

½ cup granulated sugar

1 beaten egg

3 cups sifted flour

½ tsp. baking soda

½ tsp. baking powder

¼ tsp. salt

½ tsp. almond extract

½ tsp. peppermint extract

½ cup sour cream

Cream the shortening and the sugars together. Add the egg and beat well. Add the sifted dry ingredients alternately with the flavorings and sour cream. Blend until the dough is smooth. Drop by teaspoonfuls on a greased cookie sheet. Bake in a 400° oven 10 to 12 minutes. Makes about 4 dozen cookies.

PRESSED COOKIES

Spritz

Since the Spritz cookie dough is quite rich, the ulcer patient should get his doctor's permission before eating these cookies. Spritz cookies are tastier if made entirely with butter, instead of using part vegetable shortening.

1 cup butter or margarine	2½ cups sifted flour
½ cup sugar	¼ tsp. salt
1 beaten egg	½ tsp. lemon extract

Cream together the butter and sugar until light and fluffy. Add the egg and mix well. Then add the sifted flour, salt, and flavoring. Use a cookie press to shape the cookies. (This dough may also be dropped from a teaspoon.) Bake on an ungreased cookie sheet in a 400° oven for 7 or 8 minutes or until the edges are lightly browned. For holiday occasions, decorate the cookie tops with colored sugar. Makes about 7 dozen cookies.

Chinese Pressed Cookies

1 cup butter	2 cups sifted flour
½ cup sugar	¼ tsp. baking powder
1 egg yolk	¼ tsp. salt
1½ tbsps. cream	1 tsp. almond extract

Cream together the butter and sugar. Add the egg yolk and mix until well blended. Stir in the cream. Gradually add the sifted dry ingredients and the flavoring. Use a cookie press to shape the cookies. Bake on an ungreased cookie sheet at 400° for 7 or 8 minutes. (This dough can also be rolled out on a board and cut with cookie cutters.) Makes 7 dozen cookies.

FORMED COOKIES

Cookies can be formed into shapes in several ways. If the dough is not sticky, or has been well chilled, small bits of it can be broken off and rolled into balls between floured palms. The balls can then be baked as is, pressed down with a knife or the tines of a fork dipped in flour, or flattened with the bottom of a small glass wrapped in a damp cloth. When the dough is particularly easy to handle, try shaping it, between floured palms, into thin rolls or sticks. These can be arranged on the baking sheet in crescent, ring, or pretzel shape.

Orange Cookie Balls

½ cup shortening	1 egg, separated
⅓ cup sugar	¼ tsp. lemon extract
⅓ tsp. salt	¼ tsp. orange extract
	1 cup flour

Cream together the shortening, sugar, and salt. Beat the egg yolk; then add it and the flavorings. Slowly add the sifted flour. Shape the dough into small balls, roll in unbeaten egg white, then granulated sugar. Flatten with the blade of a knife. Bake on a greased cookie sheet at 350° about 12 minutes. Makes about 2½ dozen cookies.

Orange–Lemon Cookies

1 cup butter	¼ tsp. lemon extract
¾ cup confectioners' sugar	¼ tsp. salt
¼ tsp. orange extract	1¾ cups flour

Cream together the butter and sugar. Add the flavorings, salt, and flour that has been sifted three times after measuring. Mix well. Chill for several hours in the refrigerator. Roll into small balls and flatten with the tines of a fork dipped in flour. Sprinkle cookie tops with colored sugar if desired. Bake in slow (325°) oven for 18 to 20 minutes. Makes about 3 dozen cookies.

Pineapple–Sour Cream Cookies

1½ cups sugar	1½ tsps. baking soda
1 cup butter	1 tsp. cream of tartar
2 tbsps. sour cream	¼ tsp. salt
2 beaten eggs	2 tbsps. pineapple juice
3½ cups flour	½ tsp. lemon extract

Cream together the sugar and shortening. Add the cream and eggs and beat well. Sift the dry ingredients together and add alternately with the pineapple juice. Add flavoring. Roll the dough into small balls and flatten with a fork dipped in sour cream. Bake on an ungreased cookie sheet in a 350° oven about 15 minutes. Makes about 4 dozen cookies.

Lemon Mint Cookies

1 cup butter	½ tsp. peppermint extract
½ cup light brown sugar	2 cups sifted flour
¼ cup granulated sugar	¼ tsp. salt
1 egg yolk	2 tbsps. crushed lemon stick candy

Cream together the butter and sugars. Add the egg yolk and flavoring and mix well. Add the sifted flour and salt. Form the dough into small balls. Arrange on an ungreased cookie sheet, flatten with a fork dipped in confectioners' sugar, and sprinkle lightly with crushed lemon candy. Bake in a 425° oven about 10 minutes. Makes 2½ dozen cookies.

Cindy Balls

½ cup butter	2 tbsps. half-and-half cream
1½ cups sugar	1½ cups flour plus 2 tbsps.
4 beaten egg yolks	½ tsp. baking powder
1½ tsps. vanilla extract	¼ tsp. salt

⅛ tsp. cinnamon (permanent ulcer diet) mixed with small amount of sugar

Cream together the sugar and butter. Mix in the egg yolks, vanilla, and cream. Add the sifted flour, baking powder, and salt, and blend thoroughly. Chill 3 to 4 hours. Shape the dough into small balls and roll them in the mixture of cinnamon and sugar. Place the balls 2 inches apart on a greased cookie sheet. Bake in a 375° oven for 12 minutes. Makes about 2½ dozen cookies.

Apricot Delights

½ cup butter	½ tsp. lemon extract
⅓ cup sugar	1 cup sifted flour
1 egg yolk	¼ tsp. salt

Apricot preserves, strained

Cream together the butter and sugar. Stir in the egg yolk and flavoring. Add flour and salt and mix well. Shape the dough into small balls and place on a greased cookie sheet. Make a depression in each cookie. Bake in a 300° oven about 30 minutes. Fill the depressed centers with apricot preserves. Store in a tin or cover with waxed paper. Makes about 3½ dozen small cookies.

Strawberry Buttons

½ cup butter	1 tsp. baking powder
⅔ cup sugar	¼ tsp. salt
3 tbsps. strained honey	2 tbsps. half-and-half cream
2 cups sifted flour	1 tsp. lemon juice

Strawberry jelly

Cream together the butter and sugar. Add the honey and mix well. Add the dry ingredients alternately with the cream and lemon juice. Shape the dough into small balls and arrange on a greased cookie sheet. Make a crease in the center of each cookie with a spoon and put a dab of strawberry jelly in the crease. Bake in a 375° oven for 10 to 12 minutes. Makes about 2½ dozen cookies.

Meg Sugar Balls

1 cup vegetable shortening	3 cups sifted flour
1½ cups sugar	1½ tsps. cream of tartar
3 beaten eggs	1 tsp. baking soda
1 tsp. vanilla extract	½ tsp. salt
¼ tsp. nutmeg	2 tbsps. sugar colored with a few
(permanent ulcer diet)	drops food coloring

Cream together the shortening and sugar. Add the eggs, vanilla, and nutmeg and beat until well blended. Add the sifted dry ingredients, except for the colored sugar. Chill the dough. Break off bits of chilled dough, roll into small balls, then roll in colored sugar. Place on a greased cookie sheet and bake in a 400° oven for 8 to 10 minutes, or until lightly browned. Makes about 4 dozen cookies.

Scottish Shortbread Cookies

Shortbread is rich, and the ulcer patient should therefore get his physician's permission before eating shortbread cookies. The best shortbread is made entirely with butter.

1 cup butter	1 tsp. vanilla extract
⅔ cup light brown sugar	2½ cups sifted flour

Cream the butter and sugar until well blended. Add the vanilla and mix well. Then add the flour, a small amount at a time, blending in each addition thoroughly. Pat out the dough until it is only ¼ inch thick; then roll lightly with a rolling pin to smooth the surface.

Cut the dough into squares, diamonds, or any desired fancy shapes. (This dough can also be formed into small balls or crescents.) Bake on an ungreased cookie sheet at 350° for 20 to 25 minutes, or until done. Makes about 3½ dozen cookies.

Variation: Substitute ½ cup of confectioners' sugar for the brown sugar.

REFRIGERATOR COOKIES

Refrigerator cookies are made from a rather stiff dough, which is shaped into long rolls, wrapped in waxed paper, and chilled in the refrigerator for several hours until it is firm enough to be sliced.

Ribbon cookies can be made from this dough by dividing it into two portions and adding food coloring to one of them. Then line a refrigerator tray with waxed paper, put half of the colored dough into the tray, and smooth it with a spatula. Cover this with half of the plain dough and smooth out again. Add a second colored layer and a second plain layer, following the same procedure of smoothing with a spatula. The layers should be of equal thickness. Cover the tray with waxed paper and chill for 12 hours.

When ready to bake refrigerator cookies, place the dough on a bread board. Using a very sharp knife, cut it into thin, even slices.

Rum Refrigerator Cookies

2 cups granulated sugar	3 cups flour
½ cup butter	1 tsp. cream of tartar
2 beaten eggs	¼ tsp. salt
½ tsp. rum extract	1 tsp. baking soda

Cream together the sugar and butter; add the eggs, flavoring, and sifted dry ingredients. Mix well. Shape into 1 or 2 rolls and wrap in waxed paper, folding the ends of the paper over to seal. Place in the refrigerator for 12 hours, or longer if desired. Then slice thin and bake on an ungreased cookie sheet in a 375° oven for 10 to 12 minutes.

Butterscotch Refrigerator Cookies

½ cup butter	1 beaten egg
1 cup light brown sugar, firmly packed	1½ cups sifted flour
	½ tsp. baking soda
1 tsp. vanilla extract	¼ tsp. salt

½ tsp. cream of tartar

Cream together the butter and sugar. Add the flavoring and egg and mix well. Gradually stir in the dry ingredients. Shape the dough into 2 rolls, wrap in waxed paper, and chill. Slice the dough thin and bake on a greased cookie sheet in a 400° oven for 10 to 12 minutes. Makes about 2½ dozen cookies.

Chocolate Striped Refrigerator Cookies

½ cup butter or margarine	1½ cups sifted flour
½ cup light brown sugar, firmly packed	½ tsp. baking powder
	¼ tsp. salt
1 tsp. vanilla extract	3 tbsps. half-and-half cream
1 egg yolk	½ oz. unsweetened chocolate, melted

Cream together the butter and sugar. Add the flavoring and egg yolk and mix well. Add the sifted dry ingredients alternately with the cream. Divide the dough in halves, and add the melted chocolate to one half. Shape each half into a roll—one chocolate, the other plain. Wrap the rolls in waxed paper and chill.

Divide each roll in halves by cutting it lengthwise. Press a dark half-roll and a light half-roll together. Wrap the 2 new rolls in waxed paper and chill. Slice thin and bake on a greased cookie sheet in a 375° oven about 10 minutes or until light brown. Makes about 2½ dozen cookies.

ROLLED COOKIES

Rolled cookies are a little more difficult to make successfully, but they are worth the extra time and effort. Once the technique of handling and rolling the dough is mastered, you may consider them as easy to make as any other type of cookie.

If you roll the dough on a pastry cloth and use a cover for the rolling pin, less flour will be required for the rolling. Cookies can also be rolled between two sheets of waxed paper. Whenever a dough proves unusually difficult to handle, chill it for an hour or so in the refrigerator and then try again.

Sugar Cookies

½ cup butter or margarine	¼ tsp. lemon extract
1 cup sugar	1½ cups sifted flour
1 beaten egg	½ tsp. baking powder
1 tsp. vanilla extract	¼ tsp. salt

Cream together the shortening and sugar. Add the beaten egg and mix well. Add the flavorings and the sifted dry ingredients. Chill the dough 1 hour in the refrigerator.

Roll the dough between sheets of waxed paper, using only part of the dough at a time. Cut the cookies out with fancy cutters and place them on a greased baking sheet. Bake at 375° for 10 to 12 minutes, or until light brown. (These cookies may be decorated by swirling confectioners' sugar icing on the top.) Makes about 2½ dozen cookies.

Orange—Honey Cookies

½ cup light brown sugar, firmly packed	2 tbsps. half-and-half cream
½ cup vegetable shortening	½ tsp. orange extract
½ cup strained honey	2½ cups sifted flour
2 tbsps. fresh lemon juice	½ tsp. baking powder
	½ tsp. baking soda

¼ tsp. salt

Cream together the sugar and shortening. Add the honey, lemon juice, cream, and flavoring. Stir in the sifted dry ingredients and mix well. Chill the dough for 1 hour. Then roll out to ¼ inch in thickness on a floured board and cut with cookie cutters. Bake on a greased cookie sheet in a 350° oven about 10 minutes or until light brown. Makes about 5 to 6 dozen cookies.

PASTRY AND PIES

The patient on the permanent ulcer diet may usually have plain pie fillings that contain no spices or roughage. Crust for these fillings should be made from cornflake, Rice Krispies, or vanilla wafer crumbs.

Crumb crusts are simple and foolproof to make, even for the inexperienced cook. Crush the flakes or wafers between 2 sheets of waxed paper and then mix them thoroughly with the sugar and melted butter specified in the recipes. The crusts may be used unbaked (chilled in the refrigerator) or baked.

Vanilla Wafer Crust

1⅓ cups vanilla wafer crumbs   3 tbsps. softened butter or margarine
                          2 tbsps. sugar

Mix the ingredients together well. Then press the crumb mixture firmly and evenly against the bottom and sides of a 9-inch pie plate. Bake in a moderately hot oven (375°) for 8 minutes. Chill.
Variation: Use light brown sugar.

Cornflake Crumb Crust

¾ cup cornflake crumbs   2 tbsps. sugar
                  2 tbsps. soft butter

Combine the cornflake crumbs, butter, and sugar and mix well. Press evenly and firmly around the sides and bottom of an 8-inch pie plate. Chill.

Rice Krispies Crust

3 cups Rice Krispies   2 tbsps. light brown sugar
                  2 tbsps. melted butter

Crush the Rice Krispies. Add the sugar and butter and mix well. Press the mixture firmly and evenly against the bottom and sides of an 8-inch pie plate. Bake in moderately hot (375°) oven for 8 minutes. Chill.

CREAM PIES

Caramel—Marshmallow Pie

¾ cup light brown sugar	3 eggs, separated
4 tbsps. cornstarch	1½ tsps. vanilla extract
Dash of salt	1 tbsp. butter
2 cups half-and-half cream	Marshmallows for top

Vanilla Wafer Crust

Prepare a Vanilla Wafer Crust and bake according to the recipe directions. Cool.

Mix the dry ingredients with a small amount of cream to make a paste; then add the egg yolks and mix well. Stir in the remainder of the cream and cook in a double boiler until thick, stirring constantly. Cool. Add the vanilla and melted butter and fold in the stiffly beaten egg whites.

Pour the filling into the prepared crust and arrange marshmallows over the top. Bake in a 350° oven until the marshmallows are light brown. Serves 5 to 6.

Cocoa Cream Pie

1 tbsp. cocoa	3 eggs, separated
¾ cup sugar	1 cup half-and-half cream
¼ tsp. salt	1 tbsp. butter
4 tbsps. cornstarch	1 tsp. vanilla extract
1 cup milk	Vanilla Wafer Crust

Prepare a Vanilla Wafer Crust and bake according to the recipe directions. Cool.

Mix the dry ingredients with a small amount of milk to form a paste; then add the egg yolks and blend together thoroughly. Stir in the cream and the remainder of the milk and cook in a double boiler until thick, stirring constantly. Remove from the heat and add the butter and flavoring. Cool.

Pour the filling into the prepared crust. Beat the egg whites until stiff, add 5 tablespoons of sugar, and beat again. Cover pie with the meringue and bake in a 350° oven until the meringue is light brown. Serves 5 to 6.

Vanilla Wafer Cream Pie

¼ cup sugar

3 tbsps. cornstarch

3 eggs, separated

2 cups milk, scalded

1½ tsps. vanilla extract

Vanilla Wafer Crust

Prepare a Vanilla Wafer Crust and bake according to the recipe directions. Cool.

Mix together the sugar and cornstarch. Beat the egg yolks and add them to the dry mixture, blending well. Stir in the scalded milk and cook in a double boiler until the custard coats the spoon, stirring constantly. Remove from heat and add the flavoring. Cool for a short time before pouring into the prepared crust.

Beat the egg whites until stiff, add 4 tablespoons of sugar, and beat again. Spread over the pie and bake in a 350° oven for 12 to 14 minutes. Serves 5 to 6.

Variation: For the patient on the permanent ulcer diet who is allowed to have decaffeinated coffee, 1 rounded teaspoon of caffein-free instant coffee can be added to the filling along with the dry ingredients, to make Coffee Cream Pie.

Lemon Cream Pie

4 tbsps. cornstarch

¾ cup sugar

1 cup milk

3 eggs, separated

1 cup water

Juice of 1 lemon

2 tbsps. butter

Vanilla Wafer Crust

Prepare a Vanilla Wafer Crust and bake according to the recipe directions. Cool.

Mix the dry ingredients. Add a small amount of milk to make a paste. Stir in the beaten egg yolks. Slowly add the water, the remainder of the milk, and the lemon juice. Cook in a double boiler until thick, stirring constantly. Remove from the heat, add butter, then cool. Pour the filling into the prepared crust.

To make the meringue, beat the egg whites until stiff, add 5 tablespoons of sugar, and beat again. Spread over the pie. Bake at 350° until the meringue is light brown. Serves 5 to 6.

Butterscotch Pie

1 cup light brown sugar,
  firmly packed
¼ tsp. salt
4 tbsps. cornstarch

2 cups scalded milk
3 eggs, separated
2 tbsps. butter
½ tsp. maple flavoring

Vanilla Wafer Crust

Prepare a Vanilla Wafer Crust and bake according to the recipe directions.

Mix the sugar, salt, and cornstarch with a small amount of milk to make a paste. Add the egg yolks, then the remainder of the milk. Cook in a double boiler until thick. Remove from the heat and add the butter and maple flavoring. Pour into the prepared crust.

Make a meringue by beating the egg whites, adding 4 tablespoons sugar, and beating again. Bake in a 350° oven for 12 to 14 minutes until meringue is light brown. Serves 5 to 6.

FRUIT PIES

Fruit used for pies should be cooked and strained, unless the patient's doctor directs otherwise.

Apple Tapioca Pie

1½ cups strained, cooked apples
3 eggs
5 tbsps. quick-cooking tapioca

¾ cup sugar
2½ cups milk
Juice of ½ lemon

Vanilla Wafer Crust

Prepare a Vanilla Wafer Crust and bake according to the recipe directions. Cool.

Beat the eggs. Add the tapioca, sugar, strained apples, milk, and lemon juice. Cook in a large saucepan until the mixture thickens and comes to a full boil. Cool. Then pour the filling into the prepared crust. Serve with whipped cream. Serves 5 to 6.

Florida Orange Pie

⅔ cup sugar
¼ tsp. salt

1 cup cream or milk
¾ cup orange juice

3 tbsps. cornstarch   1 tbsp. butter
3 eggs, separated   Cornflake Crumb Crust

Prepare a Cornflake Crumb Crust and chill.

Mix the sugar, salt, and cornstarch together. Add the egg yolks and blend well; then add the cream. Slowly stir in the orange juice and cook in a double boiler until the mixture coats the spoon, stirring very frequently. Remove from the heat and add the butter. Cool for a few minutes before pouring into the prepared crust.

Beat the egg whites until stiff, add 4 tablespoons sugar, and beat again. Spread the meringue over the pie and bake for 10 to 12 minutes at 350°, or until the meringue is light brown. Serves 5 to 6.

CHIFFON AND FLUFF PIES

These light, fluffy pies, so delicate and attractive in appearance, owe their airy texture to beaten egg whites, gelatin, or whipped cream. A few drops of food color can be added to deepen their natural color.

Lemon Chiffon Pie

1 envelope unflavored gelatin   ⅓ cup sugar
¼ cup cold water   ¼ cup lemon juice
3 eggs, separated   ¼ tsp. salt
                   Vanilla Wafer Crust

Prepare a Vanilla Wafer Crust and bake according to the recipe directions. Cool.

Soften the gelatin in cold water. Beat the egg yolks slightly; then add ⅓ cup sugar, the lemon juice, and salt. Pour into the top of a double boiler and cook over hot, *not boiling*, water, stirring constantly, until of custard consistency. Remove from the heat, add the softened gelatin, and stir until dissolved. Chill until the mixture is of the consistency of unbeaten egg whites.

Beat the egg whites until stiff; gradually beat in ⅓ cup sugar. Fold the gelatin mixture into the beaten whites and pour into the prepared crust. Chill until firm. Serve with whipped cream.

Peach Chiffon Pie

1½ cups strained canned peaches
1 tbsp. unflavored gelatin
¼ cup cold water
3 beaten egg yolks
½ cup sugar

¼ tsp. salt
1 tbsp. orange juice
¼ tsp. almond extract
3 beaten egg whites
Vanilla Wafer Crust

Prepare a Vanilla Wafer Crust and bake according to the recipe directions. Chill.

Soften the gelatin in cold water. Mix the egg yolks with half of the sugar, the peaches, salt, and orange juice. Cook and stir over boiling water until the mixture thickens. Remove from the heat and stir in the softened gelatin until it is dissolved. Cool until the mixture starts to congeal. Fold in the flavoring. Add the remainder of the sugar to the well-beaten egg whites and fold them in last. Pour the filling into the prepared crust and store in the refrigerator. Serves 5 to 6.

Lemon Soufflé Pie

3 eggs, separated
½ cup sugar

¼ cup lemon juice
¼ cup water

Vanilla Wafer Crust (8-inch)

Prepare a Vanilla Wafer Crust and bake according to the recipe directions.

Beat the egg yolks and then mix with the sugar, lemon juice, and water. Cook in a double boiler until thick, stirring constantly. Remove from the heat. Beat the egg whites until thick and slowly add 4 tablespoons of sugar. Fold them into the cooked filling. Pour the filling into the prepared crust and cool. Serve chilled, with a dab of whipped cream. Serves 5 to 6.

Frozen Lemon Crumb Pie

3 eggs, separated
⅔ cup sugar
Dash of salt

¼ cup lemon juice
2 tbsps. water
½ cup cream, whipped

1½ cups vanilla wafer crumbs

Beat the egg yolks well. Combine with the sugar and salt; then slowly add the lemon juice and water. Cook in a double boiler until thick, stirring constantly. Cool. Beat the egg whites and add 2 tablespoons sugar. Fold them into the mixture. Fold in the whipped cream. Put half of the vanilla wafer crumbs in the bottom of a refrigerator tray. Pour the lemon filling over the crumbs. Top with the remaining crumbs and freeze until firm. To serve, cut into wedge-shaped pieces. Serves 5 to 6.

Apricot Chiffon Pie

1½ cups apricot nectar
1 tbsp. unflavored gelatin
½ cup sugar

3 tbsps. lemon juice
1 egg white
½ cup cream, whipped
Cornflake Crumb Crust (8-inch)

Prepare a Cornflake Crumb Crust and chill.

Mix together the apricot nectar, gelatin, and sugar. Cook over hot water, stirring constantly, until the gelatin is dissolved. Stir in the lemon juice. Then cool to room temperature. Stir in the unbeaten egg white and chill until the mixture begins to set. Whip until light and fluffy. Fold in the whipped cream, pour into the prepared crust, and chill until set. Serves 5 to 6.

Red Fluff Pie

2 cups canned tart red cherries,
   drained
1 tbsp. unflavored gelatine
1 cup cherry juice
   (add water if necessary)

3 eggs, separated
⅔ cup sugar
¼ tsp. vanilla extract
Few drops red food coloring
Vanilla Wafer Crust

Prepare a Vanilla Wafer Crust and bake according to the recipe directions. Chill.

Strain the cherries. Soften the gelatin in ¼ cup of the cherry juice. Beat the egg yolks and add ⅓ cup of sugar; stir in the remaining cherry juice. Cook in the top of a double boiler until of custard consistency, stirring constantly. Remove from the heat and stir in the softened gelatin. Cool; then add the flavoring, food coloring, and cherries. Beat the egg whites until stiff and add the remainder of the sugar. Fold them into the gelatin mixture. Pour the filling into the prepared shell. Serve with whipped cream. Serves 5 to 6.

Rum Nog Pie

1 tsp. unflavored gelatin	1 cup scalded milk
1 tbsp. cold water	3 beaten egg yolks
½ cup sugar	1 tbsp. butter
2 tbsps. cornstarch	½ tsp. rum extract
¼ tsp. salt	½ cup cream, whipped
	Vanilla Wafer Crust

Prepare a Vanilla Wafer Crust and bake according to the recipe directions. Cool.

Soften the gelatin in the cold water. Stir together the sugar, cornstarch, and salt with a small amount of milk. Gradually add the remainder of the milk and cook in a double boiler until the mixture thickens. stirring constantly. Add a small amount of the hot mixture to the egg yolks and stir rapidly. Return to the double boiler and mix thoroughly. Add the gelatin and butter and stir. Remove from the stove and cool. Then add the rum extract and fold in the whipped cream. Pour into the prepared crust and sprinkle lightly with nutmeg (permanent ulcer diet). Serves 5 to 6.

Variation: On the permanent ulcer diet, 1 rounded teaspoon of caffein-free instant coffee can be added with the sugar and cornstarch (use vanilla instead of rum extract).

Banana Marlborough Pie

3 sliced bananas	½ tsp. banana extract
2 tbsps. lemon juice	¾ cup cream, whipped
20 marshmallows	Vanilla Wafer Crust (made with
½ cup milk	light brown sugar)

Prepare a Vanilla Wafer Crust and bake according to the recipe directions. Cool.

Arrange the banana slices in the prepared crust and sprinkle them with the lemon juice. Heat the marshmallows and milk in the top of a double boiler until the marshmallows are melted, stirring frequently. Cool for a few minutes; then add the banana extract and fold in the whipped cream. Pour the mixture over the bananas and chill the pie until serving time. Serve with vanilla wafer crumbs over the top. Serves 5 to 6.

Lime—Cherry Pie

1 cup dark, sweet pitted cherries,   ¾ cup sugar
   drained (permanent ulcer diet)   ¼ tsp. salt
1 pkg. lime gelatin   1 large can evaporated milk
1 cup boiling water   Juice of 1 lemon
              Vanilla Wafer Crust

Chill the evaporated milk, a beater, and a bowl in the refrigerator for 1 hour.

Prepare a Vanilla Wafer Crust and bake according to the recipe directions. Cool.

Dissolve the gelatin in the boiling water. Add the sugar and salt and stir until dissolved. Cool. Whip the canned milk until stiff; add the lemon juice. Whip the gelatin until fluffy. Combine the two mixtures and fold in the cherries. Pour into the prepared crust and top with whipped cream. Keep chilled until ready to serve. Serves 6 to 8.

Strawberry Chiffon Pie

½ cup slightly cooked   ½ cup sugar
   strawberries, strained   ¼ tsp. salt
1 tbsp. unflavored gelatin   ¼ cup water
¼ cup cold water   ½ cup cream, whipped
3 beaten egg yolks   Few drops red food coloring
        Vanilla Wafer Crust (8-inch)

Prepare a Vanilla Wafer Crust and bake according to the recipe directions. Cool.

Soften the gelatin in ¼ cup cold water. Put the egg yolks, sugar, and salt in the top of a double boiler and mix well. Add the strawberries and ¼ cup water and cook until the mixture starts to thicken, stirring constantly. Remove from the heat, add the gelatin, and stir until well blended. Cool. Then fold in the whipped cream and food coloring. Pour into the prepared crust; spread wafer crumbs on top or serve with a small amount of whipped cream. Serves 5 to 6.

Orange Chiffon Pie

1 tbsp. unflavored gelatin
½ cup cold water
½ cup sugar
¼ tsp. salt
3 beaten egg yolks

⅓ cup fresh orange juice, strained
⅓ cup water
½ cup cream, whipped
Rice Krispies

Prepare a Rice Krispies Crust and bake according to the recipe directions. Cool.

Soften the gelatin in the cold water. Add the sugar and salt to the egg yolks; then gradually stir in the water and orange juice. Cook in a double boiler until thickened, stirring constantly. Remove from the heat, stir in the softened gelatin, and cool. Fold in the whipped cream. Pour into the prepared crust and chill. Serves 5 to 6.

Orange Gelatin Pie

1 pkg. orange gelatin
1 cup boiling water
¾ cup sugar
2 tbsps. cornstarch

1 beaten egg
½ cup water
¼ tsp. lemon extract
1 cup cream, whipped

Vanilla wafers

Mix the gelatin with the boiling water and stir until it is dissolved. Set aside. Combine the sugar, cornstarch, beaten egg, and ½ cup water and cook in a double boiler until the mixture thickens, stirring constantly. Remove from the heat, add the lemon extract, and fold in the whipped cream. Whip the gelatin until frothy. Combine the two mixtures and pour into a 9-inch pie pan lined with vanilla wafers around the sides and crushed wafers in the bottom. The pie may be topped with a bit of whipped cream, if desired. Chill until ready to serve. Serves 6 to 8.

St. Patrick's Pie

1 envelope unflavored gelatin
½ cup cold water
4 eggs, separated
Dash of salt

¾ cup sugar
¼ cup lime juice
Green food coloring
Vanilla Wafer Crust

Prepare a Vanilla Wafer Crust and bake according to the recipe directions. Chill.

Soften the gelatin in cold water. Beat the egg yolks and add salt and ½ cup sugar. Slowly add the lime juice. Cook in the top of a double boiler until thickened, stirring constantly. Remove from the heat and add the softened gelatin. Stir until well blended. Add the food coloring. Chill for a few minutes. Beat the egg whites until stiff, combine with the remaining sugar, and add to the gelatin mixture. Pour into the prepared crust. Serve with whipped cream and maraschino cherries on top (cherries for decoration only). Serves 5 to 6.

Banana Rum Pie

2 bananas, mashed
1 tbsp. unflavored gelatin
¼ cup cold water
⅔ cup sugar

2 tbsps. lemon juice
½ tsp. rum extract
1 cup cream, whipped
Vanilla Wafer Crust (8-inch)

Prepare a Vanilla Wafer Crust and bake according to the recipe directions. Cool.

Soften gelatin in the cold water; then dissolve by heating over hot water. Stir in the sugar and remove from the heat. Mix the bananas with the lemon juice and add to the gelatin mixture. Fold in the rum extract and whipped cream last. Pour the filling into the prepared crust and chill. Serve with wafer crumbs sprinkled over the top. Serves 5 to 6.

ICE CREAM PIES

Rainbow Party Pie

Vanilla Wafer Crust (8-inch)
1 pt. vanilla ice cream
1 cup cream

1 tbsp. sugar
½ tsp. vanilla extract
Pastel food coloring

Prepare a Vanilla Wafer Crust and bake according to the recipe directions. Chill. About 15 minutes before serving time, spread the vanilla ice cream over the crust. Whip the cream, add the sugar and flavoring, and color with a few drops of food coloring. Spread on top of the ice cream. Keep the pie in the refrigerator until ready to serve. Serves 6 to 8.

Cherry Ice Cream Pie

2 cups canned tart red cherries,
  strained
⅔ cup sugar
3 tbsps. cornstarch

1 pt. vanilla ice cream
2 egg whites
3 tbsps. sugar
1-2 drops almond extract

Vanilla Wafer Crust

Prepare a Vanilla Wafer Crust and bake according to the recipe directions. Cool.

Mix together the sugar and cornstarch; stir in the cherries and their juice. Cook until thick, stirring constantly. Then chill thoroughly. Spread the ice cream in the prepared crust and spread the chilled cherry mixture on top. Cover with a meringue made by beating the egg whites until stiff and then beating in the 3 tablespoons of sugar and the flavoring. (Be sure to extend the meringue to the edge of the pie.) Put under a preheated broiler for a few minutes before serving. Serves 5 to 6.

SAUCES

Sauces not only add an interesting touch to any dish but can make an otherwise plain meal seem dressed up.

A good sauce is the result of a careful blending of ingredients that insures a smooth consistency and helps to bring out the flavor. Sauces that are served cold can be made several hours ahead of time and stored in the refrigerator until needed. Hot sauces, however, are best made shortly before serving time, although when circumstances prevent last-minute preparation, they can be made a few hours in advance and stored, tightly covered, in the refrigerator. Of course they must be reheated before serving.

DESSERT SAUCES

Vanilla Custard Sauce

¼ cup sugar
1 tsp. cornstarch

2 cups milk
2 beaten eggs

1 tsp. vanilla extract

Mix the sugar and cornstarch together. Stir in a small amount of milk to make a paste. Gradually add the remainder of the milk and the beaten eggs. Cook in a double boiler until the mixture coats a spoon. Remove from heat and add vanilla flavoring. Makes about 2 cups.

Vanilla Sauce

⅔ cup sugar   1 cup boiling water
1 tbsp. flour   2 tbsps. butter
                        1 tsp. vanilla extract

Mix together the sugar and flour and gradually add the boiling water. Cook, stirring constantly. When thickened, add the butter. Remove from heat and add vanilla. Makes about 1 cup.

Vanilla Mock Whipped Cream Sauce

Heaping ½ cup powdered milk   1 tbsp. lemon juice
½ cup ice water   2-3 tsps. sugar
                        ½ tsp. vanilla extract

Chill a beater and a bowl in the refrigerator for 1 hour. Pour the powdered milk and water into the chilled bowl and beat until the mixture is stiff and starts to form peaks. Add the lemon juice and continue beating for a minute or two. Stir in the sugar and vanilla flavoring. Serve immediately, as a dessert topping.

Orange Dessert Sauce

6 tbsps. orange juice   ¼ cup confectioners' sugar
1 egg white   2-3 drops lemon extract

Beat the egg white until stiff. Gradually add the sugar, lemon extract, and orange juice and beat until blended in. Serves 4.

Lemon Sauce

½ cup sugar   Juice of 1 lemon
2 tsps. melted butter   2 beaten egg yolks
                        ½ cup cream, whipped

Combine the sugar, butter, and lemon juice with the beaten egg yolks. Fold in the whipped cream last. Serve over fruits or custards.

Raspberry—Rhubarb Sauce

10-oz. pkg. frozen raspberries
1½ lbs. rhubarb

Sugar to taste
Dash of salt

¼ cup cream, whipped

Cut the rhubarb into short lengths and cook in a small amount of water until tender. Add the raspberries and simmer for 10 minutes longer. Strain. Add sugar to taste and salt, and heat and stir to dissolve. Cool. Fold in the whipped cream. Serve over custard or sponge cake. Makes about 6 servings.

Peach Sauce

3 tbsps. butter
1 cup sifted confectioners' sugar

1 tbsp. lemon juice
1-2 drops almond flavoring
3 tbsps. canned peach syrup or nectar

Cream together the butter and sugar. Add the lemon juice, flavoring, and syrup, and beat with an electric mixer until well blended. Serve over fruit custard or cake.

Orange Sauce

½ cup orange juice, heated
½ cup sugar
Dash of salt

1 tbsp. cornstarch
½ cup boiling water
2 tbsps. butter

Mix sugar, salt, and cornstarch. Slowly stir in the boiling water and orange juice. Cook over low heat, continuing to stir, until thickened. Remove from heat and add butter. Makes about 2/3 cup.

Marshmallow Pudding Sauce

1 cup marshmallow creme
¼ cup half-and-half cream

1-2 tsps. chocolate syrup
1-2 drops vanilla extract

Combine the marshmallow creme and half-and-half cream in the top of a double boiler and cook until well blended, stirring frequently. Remove from the heat and add the chocolate syrup and flavoring. Serve either warm or cold, over ice cream or plain puddings.

Meg Sauce

1 tbsp. cornstarch
2 tbsps. sugar
2 tbsps. butter
2 beaten eggs

1 cup boiling water
½ tsp. vanilla extract
⅛ tsp. nutmeg
(permanent ulcer diet)

Mix the cornstarch with the sugar, and beat in the butter. Add the eggs and stir well. Pour the boiling water over the mixture, and cook and stir over low heat until thick. Remove from the stove and add flavoring and nutmeg. Serve heated. Makes about 1½ cups.

Rum Dessert Sauce

4 beaten eggs
⅓ cup sugar

2 cups half-and-half cream
½ tsp. rum extract

Combine the eggs and sugar and mix well. Stir in the half-and-half cream. Cook in a double boiler until the mixture begins to thicken, stirring constantly. Cool; then add the rum extract. Makes about 2¼ cups.

Cherry Sauce

No. 303 can red sour cherries,
    strained (2 cups)
⅔ cup sugar

2 tbsps. cornstarch
1 tbsp. melted butter
1 tbsp. lemon juice

Combine the sugar and cornstarch; then stir in the strained cherries, melted butter, and lemon juice. Cook in a double boiler until thickened, stirring constantly. Serve heated. Makes 4 to 5 servings.

MEAT AND VEGETABLE SAUCES

Lemon Butter Sauce

⅓ cup butter, softened

1 tbsp. lemon juice

Stir the lemon juice into the softened butter until well blended. Serve immediately. Makes 1/3 cup.

White Sauce

1 tbsp. butter	¼ tsp. salt
1 tbsp. cornstarch	1 cup milk

Melt the butter in a saucepan. Stir in the cornstarch and salt and cook until well blended, stirring constantly. Add the milk slowly. Cook and stir until smooth and thick. (Increase the amount of cornstarch and butter for a thicker sauce.) Use with meats or vegetables or in casserole dishes. Makes about 1 cup.

Variations: Use buttermilk or sour cream instead of sweet milk.

Tomato Sauce

2 cups canned tomatoes, strained	⅔ cup water
1 tbsp. butter	Juice of 1 lemon
1 tbsp. cornstarch	½ tsp. onion juice (permanent ulcer diet)

Melt the butter and stir in the cornstarch. Add the remaining ingredients and cook until thick, stirring constantly. Makes about 2 cups.

Cheese Sauce

½ cup grated, mild American cheese	1 tbsp. cornstarch
	¼ tsp. salt
1 tbsp. butter	1 cup milk

Melt the butter, add the cornstarch, and stir until well blended. Add salt and milk and cook over low heat until smooth, stirring constantly. Stir in the grated cheese and cook and stir until the cheese melts. Makes 1 cup.

Variations:
1. Add ½ teaspoon onion juice (permanent ulcer diet).
2. Add 1½ teaspoons lemon juice.
3. Add hard-cooked egg slices (permanent ulcer diet).

Hard-Cooked Egg Sauce

Follow the recipe for White Sauce. When the sauce is cooked, add 2 slices of hard-cooked egg (permanent ulcer diet). Serve over asparagus, spinach, or fish. Makes 1¼ cups.

Hollandaise Sauce

3 egg yolks   2 tbsps. melted butter
¼ tsp. salt   Juice of 1 lemon
                    1 tbsp. water

Beat the egg yolks; add salt, melted butter, lemon juice, and water. Cook in a double boiler until thick, stirring constantly. Makes about 1 cup. Serves 5 to 6.

BEVERAGES

Coffee and tea are usually banned from the ulcer diet; however, when a patient progresses to the advanced or permanent ulcer diet, the doctor may permit milk flavored with coffee or tea. A coffee substitute also is often permitted then.

Orange and grapefruit juice play an important part in this diet because of the vitamin C they furnish, but they should be well diluted and served at the end of a meal, unless otherwise ordered by the doctor.

Fruit juices are refreshing and supply essential nutrients for the diet. Additional water may be added to the fruit drinks given here.

FRUIT DRINKS

Mixed Fruit Juices

Equal parts of grapefruit and pineapple juice.
Equal parts of pineapple and orange juice.
Equal parts of orange and prune juice.
Add 1½ cups of water to each 2 cups of these juice mixtures, and sweeten to taste.

Tropical Fruit Drink

1 cup pineapple juice   2 tbsps. lemon juice
1 cup orange juice   3½ cups water
                    Sugar to taste

Mix juices together and sweeten. Serve chilled. Serves 4 to 6.

Punch Cooler

6-oz. can orange-grapefruit
    concentrate
12-oz. can apricot nectar

2 cups pineapple juice
4 cups water
⅓ cup confectioners' sugar

Dilute the fruit juice concentrate with water as directed on the can. Combine with other juices, water, and sugar, and chill. Serves 6 to 8.

Grape Lemonade

Juice of 2 lemons
Juice of 1 orange

1 cup grape juice
4½ cups cold water

¾ cup confectioners' sugar

Combine the fruit juices with water and sugar. Serve chilled. Serves 8.

Pineapple Lemonade

46-oz. can unsweetened
    pineapple juice
4½ cups water

Juice of 1 orange
Juice of 1 lemon
Sugar to taste

Combine all ingredients. Serve chilled. Serves 10 to 12.

Five-Fruit Punch

2 cups pineapple juice
2 cups grapefruit juice
2 cups orange juice
½ cup lemon juice

1 small bottle grape juice
5 cups water
Sugar or white corn syrup
    to sweeten

Stir the ingredients together and chill. Serves 10 to 12.

Apricot Nectar—Pineapple Drink

12-oz. can apricot nectar
1 cup pineapple juice

1 cup water
Confectioners' sugar to taste

Mix ingredients and chill. Serves 6 to 8.

Fruit Juice Float

Fruit juices for floats should be diluted with water before adding the sherbet or ice cream. The combinations below are especially refreshing:

1. Grape juice with a scoop of orange sherbet or vanilla ice cream.
2. Orange juice with a scoop of lemon or lime sherbet.
3. Pineapple juice with a scoop of lemon or orange sherbet.

MILK DRINKS

Milk drinks not only are soothing to the stomach but help to neutralize the acid. Milk combined with fruit juices and fruit purees makes an especially appetizing beverage; buttermilk too may be combined with fruit juices. Weak cocoa is also usually permitted on the ulcer diet.

Apricot Nectar Delight

12-oz. can apricot nectar   1-2 tbsps. white corn syrup
2 cups buttermilk   1 tbsp. orange juice

Mix the ingredients together until well blended. Serves 6 to 8.

Berry Whip

2 cups canned blackberries   2 tbsps. orange juice
2 cups milk   1 tbsp. honey

Combine the ingredients and mix in a blender; then run through a wire strainer to remove the seeds. (Divide the liquid into two batches if your blender is small.) Serves 3 to 4.

Eggnog

1 egg, separated   1 cup milk
2 tsps. sugar   ⅛ tsp. rum extract or
                                       vanilla extract

Beat egg yolk, sugar, and milk together. Add flavoring and beaten egg white. Mix until well blended. Serves 2.
Variation: Add 2 to 3 tablespoons of sweetened, cooked strawberry puree to the ingredients.

Vanilla Malted Milk

1 tbsp. malted milk powder   ¾ cup milk
                                    1 scoop vanilla ice cream

Put all ingredients in a blender or shaker and mix until well blended. Serves 2.

Chocolate Malted Milk

Follow the recipe for Vanilla Malted Milk, adding 2 teaspoons chocolate syrup. Serves 2.

Plain Malted Milk (Hot)

3 heaping tsps. plain malted   1 cup hot milk
  milk powder

Shake the hot milk and the malted milk powder in a shaker. Serves 2.

Banana Milk Shake

1 banana, mashed   2 tsps. sugar
1 cup milk   1 scoop ice cream

Mix all the ingredients in a blender or beat with an electric beater. Serves 2.

Apricot Cream Nectar Shake

1 cup apricot nectar   1 scoop vanilla ice cream
                    ½ cup milk

Put the ingredients into a blender and mix well. Serves 2.

Apple Frost

¾ cup apple juice   1 tbsp. sugar
1 egg, separated   1 tbsp. lemon juice
¼ cup water   1 tbsp. honey
1 cup milk   Dash of nutmeg
                             (permanent ulcer diet)

Put all the ingredients except the egg white and nutmeg into a blender and blend until well mixed. Then fold in the stiffly beaten egg white. Dust the top with a light sprinkle of nutmeg. Serves 3.

Prunella Shake

2 cups prune juice   ½ tsp. vanilla extract
6 cups milk   1 cup vanilla ice cream
                  2 tbsps. sugar

Put all the ingredients into a large container. Transfer about 2 cups of the mixture at a time into the blender and blend until smooth. Repeat until all the ingredients are blended. Stir together and serve. Serves 8 to 10.

Peach Milk Shake

1 cup canned soft peaches   5 cups milk
½ cup sugar   1 cup vanilla ice cream
                  ¼ tsp. almond extract

Mash the peaches and sweeten them with the sugar. Add milk, flavoring, and ice cream. Transfer 2 cups of the mixture at a time to the blender and blend until smooth. Continue until all the mixture has been blended. Stir together and serve. Serves 6 to 8.

Bing Cherry Milk Shake

1 cup pitted canned Bing   2 cups milk
  cherries   1 large dipper vanilla
¼ cup sugar   ice cream

Put the cherries and sugar in a blender and blend until fruit is of a smooth consistency. Add milk and ice cream and mix until smooth. Serves 2.

Lime—Strawberry Shake

1 cup sweetened cooked   2 tsps. honey
  strawberries, strained   2 tsps. maraschino cherry
½ banana, sliced   juice
1 cup milk   1 tsp. lime juice

Combine the ingredients and mix in a blender. Serves 2.

Mint Surprise

1 pt. milk   3 tbsps. crushed peppermint candy
                    ¼ cup whipped cream

Put 2 tablespoons of peppermint candy and the milk in a double boiler and heat until the candy has dissolved. Chill. Serve with a dab of whipped cream and a light sprinkle of crushed peppermint candy on top.

Weak Cocoa

2 scant tsps. cocoa   ¼ cup boiling water
2 tsps. sugar   2 cups milk
Dash of salt   ¼ tsp. vanilla extract
                    Dab of whipped cream

Mix cocoa, sugar, and salt together. Add boiling water and cook for 2 minutes, stirring constantly. Add milk and heat to the boiling point. Remove from heat, add vanilla, and beat with a rotary beater until frothy. Serve with whipped cream. Serves 2.

CEREALS

Cooked cereals are often the first soft food assigned to a person with an ulcer or some other digestive disturbance. Ready-to-eat cereals are usually not permitted until considerably later, depending on the patient's symptoms and his doctor's advice.

Cereals include not only breakfast foods made of corn, wheat, rice, oats, and other grains, but also macaroni, spaghetti, rice (both white and brown), and various types of flour and meal. Quick-cooking rice is a great time-saver, but many people still prefer the old-style rice.

Cereals may be cooked over direct heat or in a double boiler. For the ulcer diet, quick-cooking cereals should be cooked at least 5 minutes over direct heat. When using the double boiler method, bring salted water to a boil in the top part of a double boiler, over direct heat. Sprinkle the cereal into the water and continue to cook over direct heat for 5 minutes, stirring constantly. Then place over boiling water and cook, covered, from 30 to 40 minutes, stirring occasionally.

Quick Quaker Oats

2 cups cereal   4 cups water
                         ½ tsp. salt

Cook over direct heat or in a double boiler, following the directions given above. BE SURE TO STRAIN. Serves 4 to 6.

Cream of Wheat, Cornmeal, or Farina

1 cup cereal   5 cups boiling water
                         ½ tsp. salt

Cook by the double boiler method described above. Serves 4 to 5.

MACARONI, SPAGHETTI, NOODLES

Complete cooking directions for these products are given on the package. Be sure to have the salted water boiling actively before adding the material to be cooked. Use about 3 quarts of water for a 7-ounce package. For the ulcer diet, the chief consideration is that the food be tender and completely cooked; test with a fork before draining off the cooking water.

RICE

Rice is a particularly good food for the ulcer diet because it is easy to digest, provides energy, and can be served in many ways.

In casserole dishes rice can be substituted for spaghetti or bread crumbs. It can be combined with leftover meats to make hash or can be served as a potato substitute. Mixed with strained fruit and whipped cream, rice makes a delicious dessert, and if a few drops of food coloring are added (put in the cooking water or stir into the cooked rice), the dessert can be a colorful one.

Quick-cooking rice can be cooked over direct heat, but the old-style rice should be cooked about 45 minutes in a double boiler. In either case, be sure the rice is tender and thoroughly cooked. It can be strained if a person prefers it that way.

Old-Style Rice

1 cup rice	4 cups water
	1 tsp. salt

Cook in a double boiler for approximately 45 minutes, stirring occasionally. Serves 4 to 6.

Precooked Rice

1⅓ cups precooked rice	2 tsps. butter
1⅓ cups boiling water	½ tsp. salt

Add the butter and salt to the boiling water. Stir in the rice. After it has come to a boil, cook for 2 or 3 minutes. Then cover and remove from the heat. Let stand 8 minutes before serving. Makes 1⅓ cups.

DINING OUT

The person on a permanent ulcer diet usually worries needlessly about dining out. Most good restaurants and cafeterias have a wide-enough selection of foods so that he can choose an adequate and satisfying meal.

The breakfast menu is, of course, the easiest one to select from when away from home because milk, soft-cooked eggs, toast with butter and jelly, cooked cereals, bananas or cooked fruits, and orange or grapefruit juice can be obtained almost anywhere.

Safe choices for lunch or dinner include the following: baked chicken, roast beef, broiled steak, broiled lamb chops (or macaroni and cheese may be substituted for a meat dish); mashed or baked potatoes, candied sweet potatoes (if not heavily spiced), creamed cauliflower, carrots and peas (if tender); cottage cheese; soft canned peaches, egg custard, tapioca pudding, rice pudding without raisins, plain cream pudding, baked apple or other cooked fruit, angel food or sponge cake, ice cream, plain cookies; white toast, soda crackers; milk and buttermilk.

One drawback to dining out is the use of black pepper and other strong condiments in restaurant cooking. However, the waiter or waitress will usually be able to point out which foods are heavily seasoned. The diner should also avoid such foods as bacon, ham, fried eggs, hot biscuits, soups containing fat meats, beans with pork, pickled beets, prepared mayonnaise, and all the other dishes that are on the forbidden list.

It is doubtless best not to dine out too often; however, here again the frequently repeated advice still holds: Consult your doctor and follow his recommendation.

MENUS FOR THE PERMANENT ULCER DIET

The menus given here are planned for people on the advanced or permanent ulcer diet. They are meant only as suggestions, and can be varied in countless ways, using other suitable foods. It is important not to serve the same foods too often, lest the monotony of the menus cause the ulcer patient to lose interest in food. (The patient just beginning an ulcer diet should adhere strictly to the foods and menus recommended by his doctor, selected to fit his individual case. Many of the recipes in this book, however, will be useful in carrying out the doctor's recommendations.)

An especially influential factor contributing to the recovery of an ulcer patient is a cheerful dining atmosphere. If the table is set attractively, perhaps with colored accessories, and brightened with flowers, it helps to create a relaxed and happy mood and improves the appetite and digestion. Breakfast and lunch too should be nicely served—and not just catch-as-catch-can meals. Mealtime conversation should be confined to pleasant topics; controversial subjects and family problems should not be brought to the table. In short, as far as possible, mealtimes should be happy, leisurely occasions.

A number of digestive disturbances besides ulcer are also known to be influenced by diet. Hence, the recipes and menus in this book will be useful to anyone who, for any reason, needs to avoid irritating foods. For these people, however, foods usually need not be strained.

The person on an ulcer diet is generally advised to eat often but to eat small portions. Therefore, both midmorning and midafternoon snacks are listed on the sample menus. These may be varied in content and time of serving to suit the patient's convenience or preference.

BREAKFAST

Breakfast, the "starter" for the day, should be a satisfying meal, not merely a quick snack. People who eat a nourishing hot breakfast are said to do more and better work, and to be less irritable to work with, than those who skimp on breakfast. Usually they are healthier too, and certainly they are better fortified to meet the day's problems with high morale.

Monday

8:00 A.M.

Cooked Oatmeal (strained) with Honey and Milk or Half-and-Half Cream

White Toast with Butter and Grape Jelly

Milk or Weak Cocoa

Orange Juice (diluted half and half and served at end of meal)*

10:30 A.M.

Milk and Crackers

Tuesday

8:00 A.M.

Cooked Cream of Wheat with Milk or Half-and-Half Cream

Sunflower Eggs

White Toast with Butter and Honey

Postum

Apricot Nectar (diluted)

10:30 A.M.

Buttermilk

Wednesday

8:00 A.M.

Applesauce flavored with Lemon and Honey

Cornflakes with Milk or Cream

Soft-cooked Egg

White Toast with Butter and Strained Apricot Preserves

Hot Milk Flavored with Malted Milk Powder

10:30 A.M.

Berry Whip and Cracker

*Some doctors permit orange juice at the beginning of the meal.

Thursday

8:00 A.M.
Prunes, Cooked with a Slice of Orange and Strained
Rice Flakes with Milk or Cream
Melba Toast, Apple Jelly and Butter
Hot Milk

10:30 A.M.
Weak Cocoa

Friday

8:00 A.M.
Cooked Malt-O'-Meal (strained) with Light Brown Sugar
Country Scrambled Eggs
White Toast with Butter and Strained Pineapple Preserves
Hot Milk
Peach Nectar (diluted)

10:30 A.M.
Buttermilk

Saturday

8:00 A.M.
Cooked Rice with Light Brown Sugar, Milk, and Cream
Banana with Cream
White Toast with Butter and Strained Plum Preserves
Milk
Pear Nectar (diluted)

10:30 A.M.
Apricot Nectar Delight

Sunday

8:00 A.M.
Dried Apricots, Cooked and Strained
Puffed Rice with Milk or Cream
Poached Egg
White Toast with Butter and Strawberry Jelly
Hot Milk

10:30 A.M.
Bing Cherry Milk Shake

LUNCH

Lunch on the ulcer diet usually consists of simple foods like scrambled eggs or a casserole dish, a salad, dessert, and beverage.

Monday

> 1:00 P.M.
> Creamed Asparagus
> Cottage Cheese-Peach Salad
> Day-old Bread and Butter
> Blackberry Tapioca Pudding
> Milk
> 3:30 P.M.
> Eggnog

Tuesday

> 1:00 P.M.
> Tomato Soup
> Macaroni and Cheese #1
> Melba Toast with Butter
> Mapleine Baked Apple (remove skin)
> Milk
> 3:30 P.M.
> Milk and Cream

Wednesday

> 1:00 P.M.
> Fresh Cherry Soup (cold)
> Hungarian Noodles
> Orange-Beet Salad
> White Toast with Butter
> Stewed Dried Peaches (strained) and 2 Vanilla Wafer Cookies
> Milk
> 3:30 P.M.
> Vanilla Milk Shake

Thursday

> 1:00 P.M.

Cream of Spinach Soup
Cheese Omelet
White Toast and Butter
Peach Whip
Milk
3:30 P.M.
Malted Milk

Friday

1:00 P.M.
Borscht
Baked Sweet Potato with Butter
Melba Toast
Grape Tapioca Pudding
Milk
3:30 P.M.
Weak Cocoa

Saturday

1:00 P.M.
Yum-Yum Eggs
Lemon—Cranberry Mold
White Toast with Butter
Orange Custard
Milk
3:30 P.M.
Strawberry Nog

Sunday

1:00 P.M.
Cheese Soufflé
Baked Potato with Butter
Bread and Butter
Apple Krispy
Milk
3:30 P.M.
Banana Milk Shake

DINNER

Many ulcer patients consider dinner the most interesting meal because it includes some form of meat. The dessert served at dinner is also commonly a little more elaborate than the luncheon dessert, and some people look forward eagerly to this treat at the end of the meal.

Since the day's work is over for most people when they sit down at the dinner table, this meal is often the most unhurried and enjoyable one of the day. The housewife should do everything in her power to see that nothing disturbs the relaxed atmosphere.

Although no bedtime snacks have been included in these menus, many ulcer patients find it helpful to eat a small amount of something light and easily digested, before retiring.

Monday

6:30 P.M.
Broiled Steak
Baked Potato with Butter
Harvard Beets
Pineapple Mystique Salad
White Toast and Butter
2 Honey Chews with Apricot-Cherry Fruit Blend
Postum

Tuesday

6:30 P.M.
Chicken Aristocrat
Mashed Potatoes
Carrot Soufflé
Raspberry—Banana Mold with Honey-Marsh Salad Dressing
White Toast and Butter
Angel Food Cake with Whipped Cream Frosting
Milk

Wednesday

6:30 P.M.
Raspberry Soup

Roast Squab with Dressing
Orange Sweet Potatoes
Carrot-Pea Loaf
Party Salad
White Toast and Butter
Vanilla Cheese Cake (small serving)
Milk

Thursday

6:30 P.M.

Meat Loaf with Orange Sauce
Escalloped Potatoes
Squash with Cherry Wells
Florida Salad
White Toast and Butter
Rum Nog Pie
Milk

Friday

6:30 P.M.

Baked Fish
Mock French Fried Potatoes
Honey-Orange Carrots
Orange-Peach Gelatin Salad
White Toast and Butter
Sponge Cake Delight and Fruit Compote
Milk Flavored with Hot Tea

Saturday

6:30 P.M.

Pineapple Soup
Broiled Lamb Chops
Baked Candied Sweet Potatoes
Creamed Asparagus with Eggs
Florida Salad
White Toast and Butter
Vanilla Ice Cream with 2 Apricot Delight Cookies
Milk

Sunday

> 6:30 P.M.
> Roast Beef
> Mashed Potatoes (without gravy)
> Creamed Peas
> Bing Cherry Salad with Special Fruit Dressing
> White Toast and Butter
> Apricot Parfait with 2 Vanilla Wafers
> Milk

COOKING TERMS

Au Gratin—Cooked with a covering of crumbs usually mixed with cheese.

Bake—To cook by dry heat, especially in an oven.

Baste—To moisten slightly while roasting, using pan juice or some other liquid.

Batter—A semiliquid mixture, as for cookies or cake.

Beat—To mix by stirring with a vigorous rotary motion or a rapid over, down, and under stroke.

Blend—To mix or mingle by stirring together thoroughly; also, to run through a blender.

Boil—To cook in a liquid heated to the point where bubbles rise and break through the surface.

Borscht—A Russian soup usually made with beets and served with sour cream.

Broil—To cook by direct exposure to heat.

Brush—To spread a liquid material (melted butter, milk, etc.) over the surface.

Chill—To cool, usually by setting in the refrigerator (not in the freezing compartment).

Combine—To stir, mix, or blend together.

Compote—A mixture of fruits cooked in syrup.

Condiments—Seasonings.

Confectioners' Sugar—Powdered sugar.

Cream—To blend, mix, or stir together until of a smooth, light consistency; for instance, the eggs and sugar for a cake.

Dice—To cut into small cubes.

Drain—To pour off the fluid, as in the case of separating canned fruit from its syrup or vegetables from the water in which they were cooked.

Entrée—In the U.S., usually the main dish served at a meal.

Fillet (or Filet)—A piece of lean meat or fish without bone.

Flake—To separate into small pieces.

Fold—To bring a spoon gently down and under batter, then up and over to the edge of a bowl—a method of incorporating delicate substances like whipped cream or stiffly beaten egg whites.

Frost—To cover with an icing, as in the case of a cake.

Mix—To blend into a homogenous mass.

Mousse—A frozen dessert made with sweetened and flavored whipped cream or combinations of other ingredients thickened with gelatin; usually frozen without stirring.

Parfait—A frozen dessert made with whipped cream, eggs, hot syrup, and flavoring; also a dessert with alternating layers of ice cream, fruit or syrup, and whipped cream.

Poach—To cook in boiling water until coated, as in the case of a poached egg.

Punch—A mixture of fruit juices, sugar, and water.

Puree—Food that has been cooked until thick and soft and then strained.

Roast—To cook by dry heat.

Sherbet—A frozen dessert made with fruit juice, milk or water, sugar, and egg whites.

Simmer—To cook in liquid just below the boiling point.

Soufflé—a delicate, spongy baked dish (served hot) made mostly of eggs; stiffly beaten egg whites make it light.

Steam—To cook in the vapor of boiling water.

INDEX